"I have not been provocative!"

Linnet was furious at his misinterpretation of her friendly behavior.

"No?" Justin smiled without humor. "The restlessness, the lowered voice, the eagerness to come up here with me. I'd be a fool not to have realized what you want."

"You're an arrogant, conceited, oversexed fool!" she flung back at him. "You asked for a truce and foolishly I thought you meant it."

He laughed. "So I did, my dear girl! This is a very pleasant bonus."

"Oh!" she cried in frustration, trying to believe that it was only anger that made her tremble. "You've spoiled everything!"

"In that case, I might as well blot my record properly," he murmured, lifting her chin with fingers that allowed no resistance. Then he bent to claim her mouth. . . .

Iceberg

by

ROBYN DONALD

Harlequin Books

TORONTO • LONDON • LOS ANGELES • AMSTERDAM
SYDNEY • HAMBURG • PARIS • STOCKHOLM • ATHENS • TOKYO

Original hardcover edition published in 1980
by Mills & Boon Limited

ISBN 0-373-02437-1

Harlequin edition published November 1981

CHAPTER ONE

'WHAT on earth——!'

Linnet Grant couldn't stifle the astonished words as the taxi swung into a wide drive.

'Wrong place? That's the address you gave me.' The taxi-driver's voice was aggrieved.

She shook her head, wide gold-hazel eyes staring. 'No, this is the right address. It's just that everything's changed!'

The driver looked puzzled, then remembered the labels on the large case in the trunk. 'How long is it since you've been here?' he asked, as he pulled up beneath a wide *porte-cochère* in front of the low white modern house.

'Eight years.' Linnet pulled herself together, pushed a hand through the pale red tendrils which fringed her wide forehead as she bit her lip. 'It's exactly eight years since we left for Australia. But this is a different house— my father and my sister lived in an old-fashioned place, all additions and gables and old sash-windows.'

The driver pushed his cap back on to his head, looking at his passenger with a mixture of wariness and kindly concern. 'Place been sold while your back was turned?' he suggested.

'Well, my sister still lives here. At least——' a frown creasing the candid brow—'this is the address she's always given in her letters.' She did not add that the letters were few and infrequent, the last being six months ago.

'Tell you what. You go and ring that bell; I'll wait. If your sister has moved on the people who own the place might know where she is. If they don't, one of the neighbours will. They always do.'

Linnet looked gratefully at him. The shock of finding her old home vanished and this luxurious modern building in its place seemed to have temporarily robbed her of initiative. Or perhaps it was jet-lag, she thought as she climbed out of the cab into the warm spring sunshine. Except that a flight of four hours across the Tasman Sea from Sydney to New Zealand could hardly qualify her for jet-lag!

As she walked towards the wide wooden door she noted other changes. The big oak tree was gone, a piece of vandalism which filled her with the kind of outrage her friends had learned to dread. Linnet loved growing things with a fervour which was almost a passion, and that oak figured in some of her most cherished childhood memories.

With a firm jab of her long forefinger she rang the bell, then waited impatiently, while her gaze roamed the garden, assessing just how much damage had been done. Odd how the memory of the place remained so firmly fixed in her brain that she was able to see that very little had been altered. The garden had lost its Victorian primness and there had been replacements, but although the atmosphere was now lush and sub-tropical, the framework was essentially the same as it had been when, drenched with tears, she had gazed her last on it. The magnificent magnolia still brooded in its corner, an enormous camphor laurel, all gold and green in its new foliage and the grove of melia trees, slender of trunk with graceful ash-like foliage, covered now in soft lilac panicles of flowers were still all there.

Reluctantly she admitted that whoever had reconstructed the garden had made skilful use of the framework already there. And perhaps it had been necessary to remove the oak, for it had shaded the whole front of the house almost all of the year. But she would miss it.

The opening of the door interrupted her thoughts. Linnet turned, her sensitive features unconsciously hopeful, buoyed up by the expectation of it being Bronwyn who stood there.

But it was a middle-aged woman, severe of expression, who eyed her with obvious disapproval as she enquired

'Yes?'

Somewhat thrown by the frosty voice, Linnet found her childish stammer return. 'D-does Miss Grant live here?' she asked, then taking a firm grip of herself, 'Miss Bronwyn Grant?'

The woman's mouth pursed, while the disapproval intensified.

'Not here,' she answered. 'Around the back.'

'Around the back?' Linnet was staggered, as much by the woman's unfriendly attitude as by this announcement.

'I'm sorry,' she said faintly, 'but exactly where?'

'Just——'

A man's voice fell crisply and coldly on the soft air. 'What's the matter, Anna?'

The woman turned, explaining, 'It's just somebody looking for Miss Grant. I've told her where to go.'

He came into view from inside the house, moving quietly.

Cat-feet, Linnet thought to herself. Unconsciously her pupils widened as they met his. A pulse beat rapidly in her throat.

He was tall and fair, handsome, but the quality which impressed itself on her brain was a kind of stillness, not the stillness of serenity, but that of an animal waiting for its prey.

He looked through her as if she were not there, his glance completely without interest or expression, sharpening as it went past her to where the taxi-driver leaned against the door of his vehicle, a cigarette in his lips, obviously watching them all.

'Are you planning to stay with Miss Grant?' he asked.

A cold prickle of dislike slithered along Linnet's nerves, but until she knew what the situation was she couldn't antagonise him.

'Yes,' she answered flatly. 'I'm her sister. From Australia.'

The older woman drew in a short, hissing breath as her glance flew to the face of the man beside her, but he was still looking at the taxi-driver. Then he transferred his gaze to Linnet's face, revealing such contempt that she shrank back feeling that she had been flayed alive.

After a second of unbearable tension he said, 'Then you'd better come in. Anna, tell the driver where to go.'

'I have to pay him,' Linnet protested, her considerable pride rejecting the idea of being in the same room as this handsome, frigid iceberg of a man.

What on earth was going on here?

'Anna will do that,' he told her indifferently.

But Linnet could be obstinate. '*I'll* do it,' she said, chin lifted as she walked down the two wide, shallow steps beside the woman Anna, while the skin up her back prickled with the knowledge that he was watching her.

'Everything O.K.?'

'Yes, this is the right place.' Linnet held out a note. 'Thank you.'

He gave her change, listened as the woman gave him directions and called out a jovial 'Cheerio,' when Linnet made her way back up the steps to where the man still stood, motionless as an ice statue and every bit as welcoming.

Not normally a nervous person, she found that she was moistening her lips as she came level with him; that pale unblinking stare thoroughly unnerved her. Without vanity she knew that most men looked at her slim body and fine-boned face with pleasure, not the downright condemnation he made no attempt to hide.

'Is Bronwyn not here?' she asked as she came through the door.

The hard mouth smiled, if such a humourless movement of muscles could be called a smile. 'She works,' he said, not attempting to disguise the note of disdain.

'Oh!'

Good lord, he had her completely terrorised. Of course she knew that for the last two years Bronwyn had owned her own boutique in the fashionable suburb of Remuera.

Inadequately she went on, 'I must be suffering from jet-lag, I think. I did know. It was just such a shock—

seeing the house . . .' her voice trailed away at the chilling regard he bent on her.

'I bought the house from your sister about six months after your father died,' he told her coldly. 'My name is Justin Doyle.'

He said it as though it should mean something to her. Linnet shifted the strap of her bag across her shoulder, swallowed, then said lamely, 'I didn't know. About the house, I mean.'

'Indeed?'

Obviously he didn't believe her. Stiff with anger, she retorted, 'Yes, indeed. If Bronwyn sold to you why is she still living here?'

'She is not living here. She has a flat at the back of the property. As for why——' he paused, then went on with grim derision, '—you should know that.'

'Me?' Linnet was tired. Sleep had been difficult for months past, and as she was terrified of flying, the effort of forcing herself on to the jet to actually get here had taken its toll too. She and Bronwyn had never been close; six years' difference in age and the peculiar circumstances of their upbringing had seen to that, but she had hoped for at least a 'blood-is-thicker-than-water' acceptance.

And now here was this—this *effigy* of a man, cold as ice and obviously, strangely, loathing her, regarding her as if she were some kind of moral leper. To say nothing of the woman Anna, who had once more reappeared, and stood watchfully waiting just behind them.

To her horror Linnet felt the hot prickle of tears at the back of her eyes. In a rush of words she said, 'Look, can I just go to wherever she lives without being a nuisance to anyone? I'm rather tired . . .' She groped in her bag, found a handkerchief and blew her nose defiantly, determined not to break down and bawl like a fool in front of granite-eyes Doyle and his henchwoman.

'That's just it,' the woman Anna said now. 'You can't get into the flat. Miss Grant has the key. I've just rung the boutique and they say she's out for the day and they can't reach her.'

'Make some coffee,' Justin Doyle ordered curtly. 'Miss Grant, come with me.'

Rebelliously, because she couldn't think of anything else to do, Linnet followed him down a wide carpeted corridor where the only relief from severity was the pattern of windows which looked on to a lushly foliaged courtyard, a black bowl of gold-brown bearded irises and a superb Chinese painting on silk. Linnet would have dearly loved to view it closely, but she had almost to run to keep up with the silent panther strides of the man beside her, so she was only able to give it the most fleeting of glances.

Then they were in a small sitting room, furnished in the same spare, opulent style, with wide sliding glass doors leading out on to its own tiny sandstone terrace bordered by trellises and flower beds. The ambience was Mediterranean, several leather chairs, a magnificently carved chest and a painting, a portrait of an old woman, of such stark vividness that nothing else was needed.

'Sit down,' Justin Doyle ordered, waiting until Linnet subsided into the nearest chair before continuing, 'I gather that Bronwyn doesn't expect you.'

'No.' How could she, when Linnet had only decided to leave Sydney last night? Lamely she went on, 'It was a sudden decision.'

'I see.' Those pale ice-grey eyes surveyed her with aloof lack of interest. 'Are you certain that she'll welcome you?'

This had the effect of straightening Linnet's back as she met his eyes squarely. 'I don't know that that's any of your business, Mr Doyle.'

A momentary tightening of the muscles of his jaw warned her that she had gone too far, but the tension which sprang into life died as swiftly as it had been born. He had control, she decided, and was thankful for it. A man with such innate strength would be a bad enemy; unfortunately it seemed that he had decided that that was exactly what he should be to her.

'Possibly not,' he said now, walking across to the window. Against the brilliant light his profile was harsh and uncompromising, yet beautifully sculpted, a silhouette without any sign of weakness or slack muscle tone.

He was, she owned with considerable reluctance, a man of a certain attraction, and he could not help but know it. Even across the room she could feel the raw animal magnetism which an expertly tailored suit and immaculate linen only emphasised. A man of great *mana*, she thought, remembering the Maori term; an inherent strength of character which combined with his sexual attraction an obvious intelligence to create a formidable man. Bronwyn must be aware of this. He certainly seemed to feel some sort of responsibility for her; perhaps they were lovers.

Then she remembered Anna, and wondered just where she fitted into the scheme of things. Housekeeper? Probably. She didn't resemble him at all and he'd not spoken to her as if she was any sort of relation.

She appeared then, carrying a tray set for coffee. Set only for one, Linnet was pleased to see.

When she had gone he said without expression, 'I have to go now. Please make yourself at home until Bronwyn arrives. Anna will give you lunch.'

'Thank you.' She spoke in a stifled voice, feeling a sudden tiredness which robbed her of the energy to question him or even to wonder why he had taken such an instant dislike to her.

She couldn't care less, she told herself after he had gone. It was not quite true, but it helped.

Oddly enough after the coffee she slept, waking up only when a trolley loaded with food was wheeled into the room by the silent Anna, who apparently was going to make quite sure that she didn't sully any more of the place than she had to!

'May I use the bathroom?'

The older woman nodded. 'Yes, of course. I'll show you where it is.'

It was by the front door, a marbled dream of a room in soft golds and blues with all the necessary offices and the

sort of soap which delicately scented the air. Linnet
peered at herself in the mirror, her mouth forming an O
of distress at the horrid sight she saw there. Tumbled red
hair surrounded a face with features which were shar-
pened by tiredness and pain, a gentle mouth hardened by
the severe self-control she had imposed on herself for—
how long now? Three months, she supposed. Ever since
she had realised that David Perry was falling in love with
her mother, and not with her.

Well, it was past now. They were married, David and
her young laughing mother, and she had hidden her anguish, danced at the wedding and then fled to New Zealand, unable to bear their radiant happiness.

From the frying pan into the fire, she thought sombrely. She had hoped that Bronwyn would give her shelter for as long as she needed to find a job and a place of
her own.

After the reception she had just endured she had the
strong conviction that the sooner she became independent
and moved out of Justin Doyle's orbit the better it would
be for her.

But why should he take such an instantaneous dislike to
her? Perhaps he just didn't like redheads, she told herself,
adding rather severely that it mattered not a whit what
he thought of her. Perhaps he feared she intended to
sponge on Bronwyn. Well, he'd learn soon enough that he
was wrong.

The meal was delicious, a salad with baby tomatoes
and a quiche, frothy and redolent of cheese and onions
and cream. In spite of her dour exterior Anna was a
superb cook. But after the meal Linnet felt restless, her
healthy young body needing exercise.

Prowling the room for half an hour was no help, so she
went off in search of the housekeeper, following her ears
down a side corridor to find her in an enormous kitchen
very luxuriously appointed, kneading bread.

She looked up, saw Linnet in the doorway and
frowned, asking curtly, 'Yes?'

'I'm going for a walk,' Linnet replied just as rudely.

'Up the street. I'll be back about four.'

Which only proved that if two could play at that game one of them usually felt guilty. Linnet left swiftly, red about the ears, making her way through the house to the front door, and thence, hands plunged into the pockets of her jacket, down the sealed drive to the street.

Suburbia was pretty, she decided, especially this part of suburbia, tucked away on the northern side of one of the small volcanic cones Auckland was famous for. The jaunty shout of spring was gone, but the gardens were bright with summer flowers richer and more subtle—Sweet Williams, irises and snapdragons, roses and daisy bushes and South African proteas with their bright cone-shaped blooms. The road was canopied there by jacarandas and the sweetly scented yellow Australian frangipani, delicate kowhai and sturdy karaka, variegated pohutukawa and five-fingers, and in the shady places beneath them the glowing jewel-colours of impatiens and cinerarias.

Keenly alive to beauty of any sort, Linnet especially loved gardens; slowly, as she walked, the heavy load of pain which had weighed her spirits down for the last few months began to lift. It had been a good idea, this new beginning in her own home country, she was sure, in spite of the inauspicious start.

If only Bronwyn didn't hold a grudge for that desertion so many years ago! She sighed, remembering her sister's hatred of her stepmother, Linnet's mother, who had been their father's second wife. The desire to spare her mother pain had kept her from probing into the reasons for their flight eight years ago from their home, but she was not stupid, and occasionally there had been hints enough to make it clear that Bronwyn was one of them.

And their father, that silent, taciturn man who had been so absorbed in his career as an accountant that he had come home late from the office, eaten dinner ... then retired to his study with more work.

After eight years Linnet could barely remember him; she had seen so little of him. It seemed a pity to be twenty

and unable to remember your father. There was no resemblance between them. Linnet got her red hair and her
gold eyes from her mother. Only her name Eiluned to
commemorate her father's Welsh mother formed any link
between them, and all of her friends, as well as her
mother, called her Linnet now.

Unconsciously her fingers clenched into a fist in the
pockets of her jacket. David Perry had told her—oh, so
gently, when she had blurted out the reality of her love
for him—that she saw him as a substitute father. Perhaps
he was right, but he was her first real love after the in-
fatuations and flirtations of adolescence, and the necessity
of pretending joy for her mother had strained her courage
and will to the limit.

'It's over,' she said to herself, speaking firmly to prevent the tears which filled her eyes from spilling over.
And one good thing about that humiliating confession to
David; he would see to it that her mother did not wonder
and worry about her too much. No doubt he was relieved
to come back from his honeymoon and find her letter.

For one horrible moment she thought that she was
going to break down and bawl in the street. A swift
glance around revealed that she was the only person in
sight. She had walked a mile or so to a small row of shops
on the opposite side of the road from a painted concrete
building which had the words 'Kent Street Library'
picked out in black above the doors.

Blowing her nose, Linnet made across the road and
climbed the steps into the hushed, expectant atmosphere
of the library. She would look for work in the newspaper.
The search would redirect her thoughts to a more profit-
able direction.

An hour later she emerged, went across to the sta-
tioner's shop and bought a pen, a pad and some en-
velopes. Then she returned to the library to compose a
letter applying for the position of librarian at the Kent
Street Branch.

Feeling ridiculously furtive and rather guilty, she made
a fair copy, addressed the envelope, then ran outside and

put it in the postbox, her cheeks flushed with a fugitive
colour which made her look very young, again her fingers
crossed as earnestly as any child asking for a wish.

Bronwyn was waiting for her when she arrived back, a
small, dark woman, slim, elegantly clothed, with eyes of
startling blue and a mouth which hid secrets.

'A cable might have been a good idea,' she commented
after the initial greetings.

'I didn't really think,' Linnet confessed, feeling guilty.

'Not to worry. But I'll bet you were a shock to Justin.'

'Not as much as the place was to me.'

There was a short silence, then Bronwyn picked up her
bag, saying, 'Well, let's adjourn to the flat, shall we?'

'I'll go and thank the housekeeper.'

'Anna? O.K., do that. I hope she looked after you
well.'

Almost as if Bronwyn were the lady of the house.

Linnet tracked Anna down in the kitchen, proffered
thanks which were received with cold courtesy, then re-
joined Bronwyn in the small sitting room, where her sister
was standing staring at the painting of the old woman.

'Beautiful, isn't it?' Linnet murmured.

'It's a Clark.'

'Bobby Clark?'

Bronwyn nodded. 'Yes. He didn't want to sell it, but
what Justin wants, Justin gets—even if it's the favourite
painting of the famous Bobby Clark. Come on.'

The flat was at the back of the section, separated from
the enormous double garage of the main house by a high
wall and its own smaller garage, inhabited at the moment
by a sports car painted bright red.

'It pays to advertise,' Bronwyn told her flippantly,
observing Linnet's glance at the car. 'Come on in and I'll
get you a drink. I need something a little stronger than
coffee, but I'll make that for you if you want it. Or there's
an assortment of other stuff.'

The 'other stuff' inhabited a cupboard in a scrubbed
pine dresser in the dining room. Linnet stared at the
array of bottles, said, 'Sherry, please,' and watched as her

sister poured it into a crystal glass, then made herself a gin and tonic.

'Well—here's to luck,' she said, and then, 'Come into the sitting room. It's through here.'

It was a small room, furnished very conventionally with chairs and sofa of dark brown velvet and not much else.

'It looks like a motel, I know,' said Bronwyn, her blue eyes very shrewd as they rested on Linnet's expressive countenance, 'but it does me. Now, sit down and tell me exactly why you're here.'

Linnet told her, even the humiliating experience of having fallen in love with the man who was to be her stepfather. Bronwyn listened carefully, her expression giving nothing away.

When Linnet's clear tones faded she nodded. 'Yes, getting away was probably the best thing to do. But you've created one hell of a problem by turning up here, you know.'

Chilled by the objectiveness of this remark, Linnet shifted uneasily in her chair. 'Why does Mr Doyle dislike me so?' she asked.

'Perceptive of you. Because he thinks you're being nasty to me—to whit, claiming one half of Dad's estate.'

Linnet stared. '*What?*'

Shrugging offhandedly, her sister sipped her drink. 'Well, I wasn't to know you were going to turn up. And it was more convenient for me to stay here.'

'What on earth are you talking about?'

'Justin Doyle, mainly. I intend to marry him.'

Linnet shot a cautious glance across the room, met the cool mockery of her sister's eyes and said, 'Obviously there's a connection, but I can't find it. Mind explaining?'

'Not in the least. I first met Justin just after Dad died. He heads Doyle's Corporation, which has a finger in lots of pies; Dad had dealings with them. Justin came to offer help and suggest I sell the place to him.' Bronwyn took another sip of her drink, went on reflectively, 'You've seen him. What did you think of him?'

'Ah—well——' Linnet squirmed. 'He's good-looking—a bit too handsome, if anything.'

'And?'

'He has all that it takes.'

Bronwyn smiled. 'It's not like you to be inarticulate; if I remember correctly as a child you used to talk constantly. So I presume that he had exactly the same effect on you as he does on most women. Me, too. That aura of power really got me. The attraction was mutual, I could see,' she glanced complacently down at her superb figure. 'Mind you, he's had plenty of other loves, so I knew I had to come up with something different. I did.'

'And that was?' Linnet spoke quietly, aware that this was a sister she had never known existed, a woman with brains to make the most of her beauty and a cool calculation which was, in its way, as frightening as the leashed violence she had sensed behind the magnificently controlled mask Justin Doyle presented to the world. She should be angry with Bronwyn, but she was not; fascinated would be a more appropriate word.

'Marriage, my dear. He married a child of eighteen about ten years ago and it was the most horrendous mistake. I've been showing him for the past six months that I would be the perfect wife for him.'

Linnet frowned. 'What happened to his first wife?'

'Dead.' Her sister's shoulders lifted. 'An accident, so they said, but local rumour hath it that she committed suicide. She's irrelevant, except as the experience affected Justin.'

Repelled by the calm dismissal of the tragedy, Linnet stared across the room, noting the thick white eyelids which made Bronwyn's trick of half-hiding her eyes as she talked so effective.

'I'm shocking you,' her sister observed after a moment. 'Do you think I'm unprincipled and hard?'

'You sound it.'

'Then listen to this,' she leaned forward, speaking with a conviction which seared itself into Linnet's brain. 'I want Justin as I've wanted no other man before, and I intend to make him happy.'

'You'd better!' Linnet returned with a glimmer of humour, trying to ease the tension. 'He doesn't strike me as the sort of man who takes philosophically to disappointment.'

Bronwyn's eyes widened so that for a moment she looked frightened. 'You're right, of course. Believe me, I've thought it out very carefully.' She took another tiny sip at her drink.

'Well, to continue. When he bought the place I was desperate for a way to stay close to him. I knew I had to; he wanted me, but not enough to pursue me. I had to stick around and there were no houses for sale anywhere near. Then I saw the plans, and I got an idea. The architect had put this in as the housekeeper's flat. I told him that you'd contested Dad's will and wanted your half share and that I couldn't afford a house. He knew what I was up to, of course; he's a clever man and what he doesn't know about women isn't worth knowing.'

She paused, smiling reminiscently. Feeling faintly sick, Linnet got up and walked across the room, her skirt swishing gently as she moved.

'If he knew what you were doing why does he think I'm some sort of Jacob swiping your birthright?' she asked.

'Oh, he believed *that*. About the will, I mean. But he knew darned well that I could have rented a place. No, he thought I wanted an affair.'

'Oh!'

Bronwyn laughed softly. 'Yes; he was amused, but quite willing. So he offered me this flat and then I refused to play.'

'Wasn't he angry?'

'No, he was intrigued. Which was just what I wanted. And things have gone on from there. I'm accepted by his friends now as his girl-friend, rather different from his lover. But you can see why your arrival is hardly opportune.'

'Yes.' Linnet moved away from the window, trying to subdue the dismay which had been increasing within her for the last half hour or so. 'I'll go if you like,' she offered.

The older girl pondered, sipping her drink with a shuttered expression, those heavy lids lowered so that any emotions were carefully hidden. 'I don't think it's necessary,' she said at last. 'I can manage him.'

'If we're supposed to be at daggers drawn, you and I, you're going to have to think up a pretty powerful explanation.'

A low chuckle was her only answer, and, 'Don't enquire too deeply. Do you mind being considered a selfish bitch by him?'

Linnet shook her head, the soft pale curls picking up a stray sunbeam so that for a moment she was aureoled by radiance. 'Not particularly,' she replied slowly, remembering the icy contempt, the arbitrary treatment he had subjected her to.

'Ah, I'd forgotten—your stepfather. I suppose you won't be worrying much about any man's opinion until you get over him. You've got to hand it to Jennifer, she's got something. To be able to put her daughter in the shade!'

But Linnet wasn't going to hear her mother spoken of in this manner. 'She didn't know,' she said crisply, 'and she's just the same as she ever was—a darling.'

'Phew!' Bronwyn smiled sardonically. 'Well, that's a matter of opinion. My eyes have never been blinded by love, so perhaps I see her better. Anyway, we won't squabble over her. I might even invite her to the wedding. You'll be over the suave Mr Perry by then, and I'd like to show her the sort of man her despised stepdaughter managed to land.'

'She doesn't despise you,' Linnet retorted swiftly, though she knew it would have been wiser to say nothing.

Bronwyn gave her a disbelieving glance. 'Let's leave it, shall we? We'll never agree. Now, what have you in mind for a job? I might be able to find you something in a boutique, though the pay's not particularly good. You've done something like that, haven't you?'

'Yes, I worked part-time in a dress shop in Vaucluse. Mum liked me at home most of the time.'

'Don't sound so defensive. Who am I to criticise your upbringing? Did you enjoy your part-time job?'

Remembering how she had had to try to convince large ladies of their true size, Linnet sighed. 'Sometimes. But I might have something else.'

After she had told her sister of the position at the library Bronwyn nodded.

'Yes, I can see you there. Do you still write?'

Linnet looked her astonishment. 'How did you know?'

'Oh, I remember lots of things. You were a likeable creature—I missed you when you left. So you still scribble.'

'Yes. I've tried everything, but I like doing children's books most.'

She did not say that it was only in the discipline of writing that she had been able to forget the ever-present ache in her heart when she realised that David could never love her, or that she had a fantasy novel half finished which she hoped might be at last good enough to submit to a publisher.

'I suppose it could be quite lucrative,' Bronwyn remarked idly. 'If you're any good, that is. Well, I suppose I'd better think about dinner. No, I don't want any help. You unpack your things.'

As she hung her clothes in the small wardrobe of the second bedroom Linnet told herself that she should be relieved that Bronwyn had accepted her presence so calmly. It had been horrifying to see the depths of her dislike of Jennifer revealed, but at least the emotion didn't seem to extend to Jennifer's daughter. Unless she had exorcised it by casting her in the role of the grasping sister.

Well, only Justin Doyle knew of that—and he didn't matter. Then remembering the housekeeper's less than enthusiastic behaviour Linnet amended that to Justin Doyle and Anna. Except that he didn't seem the sort of man to confide in his housekeeper. And really, there could be no reason why she should care what either of them thought of her!

After dinner Bronwyn excused herself without saying where she was going. It took little perception to realise that she was off to see her landlord. No doubt to explain her greedy sister's continued presence! Feeling rather prickly between the shoulder blades, Linnet took a shower, then, for the evening was warm, climbed into a thin cotton wrap and wandered around, unable to settle to anything. There were few books, and those mostly fashionable coffee table things, pretty as a picture but with little meat to them. After flicking through a couple, Linnet resumed her pacing, wishing that she hadn't walked into the kind of situation she most dreaded. Now that she knew the reason for Justin Doyle's antagonism she couldn't blame him, especially if he loved Bronwyn. But she rather felt that her dislike of him would have been instinctive, he was too arrogantly imperious for her to ever feel relaxed in his presence. Perhaps that disaster of a marriage had hardened him; perhaps he had been born inflexible, but try as she would, and she rather prided herself on her imagination, she could not visualise those cold pale eyes softened into tenderness, or the cruel line of his mouth ever relaxed. Passion, yes, but not love. It was to be hoped that Bronwyn knew what she was doing.

Yes—Bronwyn. A frown marred the smooth line of her brow as she thought of her sister. So—so self-contained, almost as hard in her feminine way as the man she wanted to marry. And that marriage the result of a well thought out plan of campaign, as if it were a military operation. Did she love him? Who could love an iceberg? Yet there had been a note of something close to desperation in her voice when she spoke of him, and those blue eyes had become irradiated with a blaze of the most intense feeling.

A shiver touched Linnet's skin. Such dark emotions, and all for a man who had made one wife so unhappy that rumours of suicide were accepted without qualms! Possibly Bronwyn was tough enough to cope with him. For herself, Linnet decided the sooner she moved off the better. His glance seemed to leave weals on her skin, a most uncomfortable sensation. He must be very mercenary if the idea of Bronwyn losing money affected him so strongly.

Yet that house, obviously luxurious, had been furnished with a kind of spare austerity which had impressed her. Not the house of a man who loved money for itself. It had almost a monastic severity about it. Probably dreamed up at great expense, by a fashionable interior decorator, she thought wisely, ignoring the fact that it had mirrored his personality with subtle exactness.

A knock on the door made her look in something like panic at her scanty attire. It couldn't be Bronwyn; she had her key.

'Coming!' she called out, diving into her room and yanking on a pair of jeans and a cotton shirt.

Her relief when she realised it wasn't Justin Doyle made her smile. And Linnet's smile was famous in its way, an affirmation of genuine amusement with more than a glint of mischief.

The recipient responded in kind. 'Hey!' he exclaimed, 'are you the wicked sister?'

'Yes.' The amusement vanished from her expression.

'Sorry. No, don't look at me like that. We're two of a kind, you and me. I'm the rotten cousin.'

Against her will she lifted enquiring brows at him, seeing a younger, more dissipated-looking version of Justin Doyle, with ready laughter in the grey eyes and a weakness about the chin and mouth which rendered his undeniable good looks somewhat rakish. He looked fun, and quite untrustworthy.

'Aren't you going to let me in?' he asked coaxingly. 'I promise not to ravish you or run off with the teaspoons. I might drink a bit much of Bron's carefully chosen booze, but even drunk I'm amiable. Which is more than can be said for Justin.'

'I beg your pardon?' Linnet's mind boggled at the picture of Justin Doyle drunk!

He laughed outright at that. 'That could have been better said. My masterful cousin doesn't, of course, get drunk—he's too conscious of his dignity for that. But then he's never amiable, either, even though he's sober all the time. Now me, I'm always amiable. Come on, move away from that door,' he added. 'I've been here before, you know. Your sister doesn't like me, but as Justin puts up with me she's too afraid to show her dislike openly.'

'Who are you?' Linnet asked, reluctantly leading the way into the sitting room. The sun had moved far enough to the west to come straight into the room so that it was hot and stuffy. She pushed the sliding doors wide open to let fresh air in, and felt that the room was too small.

'Stewart Doyle.' Like her he gazed around, but he frowned in distaste. 'About as much character as custard,' he remarked. 'You'd think Bronwyn would have done something to it, wouldn't you? She's got the expertise. But she views this as a temporary pad, of course. Next stop—and final one—the big house.'

Linnet frowned, angered by the note of jaded insolence in his voice. 'If you're going to be offensive, you'd better go!'

'Believe me, you pretty little thing, I'm not being offensive. I admire the girl immensely.' He mimed elaborate respect. 'She's got old Justin thinking seriously of marriage, which is more than anyone since his little Alison has been able to do. Now, what would you like to drink?'

'Nothing.'

Grinning, he made his way over to the dresser and opened the door. 'If you thought that would prevent me, you've a lot to learn, darling. I'll fix myself something— sit down and stop standing poised for flight. I promise you I'm harmless. All the girls I've made love to have been more than willing partners. I don't smash up the furniture and I don't flake out on the floor.'

Against her will Linnet laughed. He had charm, and a

genuine appreciation of a woman's mind, speaking in a droll manner which probably was a necessary part of his stock-in-trade.

'That's better,' he returned approvingly. 'And because you laughed I'll only have a very weak drink.'

'If you have all these virtues why are you the rotten cousin?' she asked demurely.

'Virtues? They aren't virtues, my love. I do have a few of those, but not many. It's my vices which are important. And the biggest of those, according to my respected cousin and the rest of society, is that I don't accord the acquisition of money its proper appreciation.' He grinned, sat down and took a reasonable sample of his drink. 'I prefer spending it. Sometimes, alas, I spend Justin's. He doesn't like that.'

Remembering the icy inflexibility of Justin Doyle, Linnet couldn't repress a shiver.

Stewart Doyle must have been watching more closely than he seemed, for he gave a mocking but sympathetic smile. 'Exactly. He's a tough man, our Justin. Ruthless, you could say. At the moment I'm paying for my sins by being kept under his eye. And on his purse-strings.'

Not a very pleasant position, Linnet had to own. One could expect justice from Justin Doyle, but presumably of mercy there was none. 'What do you do?' she asked.

'Me? Oh, I'm a sort of general factotum.' When she raised her eyebrows at him he gave her a charming, lop-sided smile. 'Dull stuff. Let's talk about you instead. I know that you and Bron had different mothers, but try as I will I can't see the slightest resemblance to your father in you. You must have got that Titian hair and those great golden eyes from your mother.'

Linnet nodded, aware of the painful contraction of her heart which inevitably followed any mention of Jennifer, now so happily David's wife.

'I thought as much. And what dire emergency forced you across here, when you must have known that Bron doesn't exactly view you with approval?'

'That's hardly your business,' she retorted crisply, angered by his blatant curiosity. 'I shan't be here for long. As soon as I can I'll get myself board.'

Not in the least put out by the edge in her voice, he murmured, 'Justin frighten you off, did he? I don't blame you at all. He's a bad enemy, is Justin. Poor Alison found that out. She was his first wife, you know.'

He drained his glass, set it down on the table by his chair and sent a swift, malicious glance across the room.

'You're dying of curiosity, aren't you? So's Bronwyn, but I won't tell her anything about it, and she's too afraid to ask Justin. I don't mind telling you, though.'

'I don't want to hear it.' It was a lie, however. She did want to know, but not from this man who seemed to enjoy the prospect of raking up an old scandal. 'I could quite easily tell Bronwyn, you know.'

'You won't.'

His conviction surprised her so that she turned a startled face to him.

'You have integrity. I recognise it, because I haven't got it. Justin has it too, but he can't see it in you because you look like Alison, and because he believes Bronwyn.'

CHAPTER TWO

'I—I LOOK like——?'

'Yes. Saw it instantly. So did he, apparently. That's one of the reasons why he froze you to splinters. Alison had that red hair, a bit more coppery than yours, but it was cut the same, short and wispy. And her eyes were green-hazel, not pure gold, but you share that milky skin and the dark brows and lashes.'

He got up, wandered across and refilled his glass, leaving Linnet astounded, yet somehow not so surprised after all. A deep conviction had told her that Justin Doyle did not dislike her only because he believed her greedily demanding half of Bronwyn's inheritance. But how he must have hated the wife who had died so unhappily!

Over his shoulder Stewart Doyle said, 'She was tall, too, and walked like a cat, delicate movements with that same awkward grace. Only she didn't have a generous mouth like yours, and you look strong and honest. She wasn't.'

'You loved her,' Linnet said softly.

A sudden movement spilt some of the liquid from his glass. Cursing, he pulled out a handkerchief and wiped his hand, and the floor, before sinking into the chair, raising his glass to her in a mock toast.

'Clever, too. Alison was stupid. Yes, I loved her—oh, not the love of a lifetime, just a boy's crush, but it hurt. She had a way of laughing as if she alone could see an exquisite joke—it used to drive me mad. Justin fell for her in a big way. He was twenty-three, and he wanted her. I think she knew that she wasn't for him, but he was always a masterful man and she wanted his money. Him too, to a certain extent. He had a kind of fascination for her.'

Linnet didn't want to hear any more. This man was too perceptive, saw too much in spite of his weaknesses—

or perhaps, because of them, and she didn't want to be made to relive old sorrows or suffer with others. Her own pain, because of her propensity, was almost too much for her to bear.

'Don't tell me any more,' she said crisply, springing to her feet. 'I don't want to hear; none of it's my business.'

She made to walk across to the window, but he caught her hand and kept her still, his expression sardonic. He was not drunk, but he had had more than was good for him, yet there was a keen intelligence in the glance he directed at her and his grip on her wrist was strong.

'Why do you *do* this to yourself?' she demanded impatiently.

'Want to try and reform me?' he asked, laughing.

He was still laughing when Bronwyn and Justin Doyle came into the room. Linnet met the searing contempt in Justin's glance, felt a heat in her cheeks which made her angry and with a swift jerk of her wrist freed herself.

'Oh, *Stewart*!' Bronwyn's voice was delicately scornful. 'Trust you to come bothering Linnet the moment my back is turned!'

He grinned, apparently unperturbed.

'Darling Bron, I wasn't bothering her at all, merely filling her in on a few details. She's rather a darling, isn't she?'

'I'll take you home,' Justin Doyle said curtly; after that first piercing scrutiny he had not looked anywhere but at his cousin.

Stewart shook his head. 'No, thanks. I'm happy here.'

'On your feet.'

The words were spoken softly, almost without expression, but they jerked Stewart Doyle upright as if he were on wires and Linnet felt a ripple of naked fear. Suddenly the idea that Alison Doyle had killed herself rather than go on living with this man did not seem so unbelievable at all.

After they had left Bronwyn asked sharply, 'What was that drunk doing here?'

'Just talking.' Linnet had rather liked Stewart, but one look at her sister's tight expression was enough to make it clear that now was no time to say so.

'Don't let him in if he comes again. He's a damned nuisance.' The older girl picked up his glass and with a gesture as foreign as it was unexpected, hurled the contents through the open window. 'He makes me sick,' she said curtly, 'wasting his life.'

'He doesn't seem terribly happy.'

Bronwyn gave her a cold stare. 'He's had all of the advantages. Justin has bailed him out of trouble time and time again, and all he does in return is drift and run up debts.'

Another aspect of Justin Doyle's character. He must have some of the normal affections, or he wouldn't help Stewart. Then remembering the icy menace of that command, Linnet wondered if perhaps he merely hated the thought of one of his name being hauled through the courts. Yes, that was more like it.

A yawn split her face. Everything suddenly caught up with her, rendering her limp and boneless, so tired that she could barely lift her feet.

'You'd better go to bed,' Bronwyn told her, her voice level and without expression. 'Your eyes are burning holes in your face. Goodnight.'

'Goodnight.'

Sleep came swiftly even in the strange bed. When Linnet woke the next morning the flat was eerily silent. A note on the table told her why.

'I leave at 7.30,' Bronwyn had written. 'Help yourself to food. Have you any money? If not, ten dollars in the back pages of telephone directory. Go to shops and get tomatoes, vegetables and soap powder. B.'

Short and to the point. Peremptory, even. But at least she wouldn't feel quite so much that she was trespassing on Bronwyn's hospitality if she did a few messages for her.

It was a warm morning, the sun high enough in the sky to tell her that she had slept late. Trying to work out whether daylight saving made it earlier or later than the sun suggested, she squeezed yellow-orange tangeloes for juice, poached the last egg and made toast, discovering from her perusal of the pantry that Bronwyn seemed to live on gourmet foods like tinned artichoke hearts or plain cottage cheese. Nothing in between. No doubt she ate sparingly to keep that wonderful figure, and used the exotics to whip up meals for guests. But surely she ate more than cottage cheese.

The butter from the refrigerator was rock-hard, but it melted immediately. Linnet wiped a drip from her cotton housecoat with a cloth, deciding not to change into clothes until after she had eaten. Jennifer had loathed 'slopping around' as she called it, so it added a sinful edge of pleasure to the morning to be still in her housecoat.

As she ate with her customary excellent appetite she allowed her eyes to roam, wondering why Bronwyn had not cared to express any of her personality in this place. It was as bare of character as any motel room—neat, clean, quite lacking in individuality. It was odd, for Bronwyn was creative and had style; perhaps Stewart Doyle was right when he said that she thought of the flat as a mere fill-in until she married Justin.

The thought of Justin gave her a cold shudder. Pushing the memory of his presence in the flat last night from her mind, she carried her dishes to the sink, poured a cup of coffee and sat herself down again at the small table in the window which caught the morning sun. It was cooler than it had been the day before, but the sun blazed cheerfully in, gilding the small patch of grass outside, warming the colours of the Sweet Williams and alyssums and irises in a bed along the wall which separated the flat from next door.

The radio surprised her with the call of a bird; a *riroriro* or little grey warbler, so the announcer told her. It was an amusing way to announce the news and the time, and as Linnet had recognised it she began to feel more at home in the country of her birth. The coffee was delicious, the pleasant scent of it stronger by far than that from several roses in a vase on the breakfast bar.

It was unfortunate for her peace of mind that the bell should ring. With a harassed glance at her housecoat and the thought that if people were going to make a habit of catching her in undress she would have to climb into clothes first thing in the morning, she went across and without opening called out, 'Who is it?'

'Justin Doyle.'

'Wait a moment, I'll——'

'I can't wait,' he interrupted curtly. 'I'm in a hurry.'

Well, the housecoat was not in the least transparent. Shrugging, she opened the door, hoping that her too expressive countenance didn't reveal the emotions he aroused in her.

'Come in,' she invited politely, leading the way into the sitting room. 'I'm afraid Bronwyn's already at work.'

'I know. It's you I want to see.'

'Oh.' For the life of her she could think of nothing more sensible to say and he was not helping in the least, looking at her as if she was something rather nasty from under a stone. 'Would you like to sit down?'

'I won't be here for long.' He walked across to the window, stood with his back to it so that she couldn't really see his features and went on crisply, 'Exactly how long do you plan to stay here?'

Equally crisply she returned, 'Until I find a job and board.'

'I see. Then I can offer you a position in the office of my firm.'

Faintly, quite convinced that she had misheard, she asked, 'What did you say?'

'There's a position in the office of my firm in the city. It's yours if you want it.'

For some reason she became extremely angry. 'No, thank you,' she told him with a frigid courtesy which matched his. 'I've already applied for a post as a librarian. I have no skills which would make me a suitable applicant for a job in an office.'

There was a moment of silence before he said without expression, 'I see. At least you're honest. Where is the library job, then?'

'You really don't need to worry yourself about me,' she

replied smoothly, hating him for his superior attitude. 'I don't intend to be an imposition on Bronwyn for any longer than I can help.'

'You knew that you would be an imposition,' he said with harsh distinctness. 'If you have any finer feelings at all you would never have come here to put such a strain on her. Family feeling is something she possesses to a foolish degree, but you have none, or it would have prevented you from trying to deprive her of an inheritance which is rightfully hers. No doubt your mother taught you to be greedy, but surely you possess enough finer emotions to see what an intolerable position you've put Bronwyn in!'

If he had not spoken of her mother Linnet would have retained her hold on her temper. But to hear that Jennifer, who had had to be so careful and economical all these years, categorised as greedy brought the blood to her cheeks and a red mist of fury before her eyes.

'You have no right to malign my mother,' she retorted tightly, but with extreme formality. 'You've never met her and you know nothing about her. Until you do I suggest that you keep your cynical observations about her to yourself. Now if you'll excuse me, I need to get changed. You can be quite sure that as soon as I can, I'll be gone. And,' with a look which should have dropped him in his tracks, 'you obviously feel that Bronwyn's concerns are of interest to you. Please believe me when I say that my affairs are my own. I'll thank you for no interference, even if it's well meant. I can do without your particular brand of arrogance!'

It was probably the longest speech of her life; it was certainly the most stilted, each platitude delivered with a scorching anger which rendered it vibrant with sincerity. If he had insulted her she would not have cared in the least, but to impute such mean motives to her gentle, laughing mother was more than she could bear.

Buoyed up by anger, she waited for him to go, clenched hands pushed deep into the pockets of the housecoat, her gaze molten gold on the darkness of his features.

He moved so that the light fell on his face. Linnet had thought that she cared nothing for him; she realised now that he had the power to frighten her as well as anger.

A strange kick in her stomach told of her fear, but she met his icy glare with a brave attempt at composure, refused to back down or be intimidated by the implacable hostility she saw in his features, the cruelty of his mouth.

When he spoke his voice was soft, yet there was no hint of weakness there. He was angry, and compared to his anger hers had been like a flash fire, searing but soon over. His would be slow to fade, if ever it did; she had made an enemy for life, perhaps.

'You've been very frank,' he said, almost with indifference. 'I'll be the same. If you upset Bronwyn in any way, I'll make you pay for it—ten times over.'

A cold sweat touched Linnet's temples, but she refused to give way to it. 'Thank you for the warning,' she retorted flippantly. 'I doubt if you've the means, but go on thinking that you can, if it gives your ego a boost. Now, having worked off your spleen, would you like to go? I've got things to do too. I'll tell Bronwyn you called.'

For a moment she nearly ran, for he came towards her with that noiseless tread of his, purpose strong in his expression.

Her nerve held. Without flinching she endured his approach, jutted her chin as he lifted it so that he could scrutinise her pale face with its wide cheekbones and small, round determined chin. Thankful that her long lashes prevented him from seeing into the depths of her eyes, she did not attempt to meet the icy dominance of his, but contented herself with staring defiantly at his mouth. It was rigid with control, but there was a hint of a softer side to his character in the sensual lower lip.

Lucky for Bronwyn, she thought, made frivolous by extreme tension.

After what seemed to be hours but was really only seconds he released her, turning away as he said coldly, 'Your youth is some excuse for your pertness, I suppose, but don't push your luck. I don't like adolescents.'

Which was a pretty devastating parting shot, she owned reluctantly. At twenty she considered herself well past the sighs and humours of adolescence; it was rather clever of Justin Doyle to hit out at her confidence in such a way.

But then he was a clever man. Bronwyn had told her so and she had seen it too. Still, she thought to reassure herself, she wasn't stupid either. She had wanted to go to university, but Jennifer had not been well, so she had stayed at home, helped in the house and worked the middle of every day at the dress shop. An empty existence, but she had been warmed by her mother's love. And she had had time to write.

As she pulled on a light pair of slacks and a blouse she thought that perhaps she could go part-time to the university at Auckland, or take subjects extra-murally, and registered the decision to make enquiries.

There was little need for housework, but she did it anyway, to find herself only halfway through the morning with time on her hands. Almost without thought she took out the manuscript of her book, sat down at the kitchen table with a cup of coffee and began to read it. That led to corrections and before long she was busy writing, surroundings forgotten, the nasty little incident with Justin Doyle wiped from her memory as if it had never happened.

Well after lunchtime she lifted her head, flexed her tired fingers as she looked ruefully at her watch. Writing always made her ravenous, and as there was precious little in that pantry to stay her appetite, she picked up her purse and headed down the drive.

The day had fulfilled its promise, scorching hot with barely a breeze to temper it. Whoever had set out the garden had planted a wide shrub bed to hide the drive from the rest of the garden. The plants were small yet, but in a few years would form a dense screen. Right at the end, by the road, was one of the original trees, an enormous jacaranda, and perched up in a nest made by the smooth branches was a child. She was reading, but as Linnet came towards her she closed the book and looked down with a flicker of curiosity in the clear, pale eyes which branded her immediately as Justin Doyle's daughter.

'Hello.'

Linnet stopped. 'Hello.'

'You must be Miss Grant's sister from Australia.'

'Yes, I am.'

The child surveyed her with some of her father's cool aloofness. 'I'm Sarah Doyle. What's your name?'

'Linnet Grant.'

The unfamiliar name brought a slight frown to the child's face. She attempted it, stumbled and said, 'Linnet? Like a bird?'

'If you like. That's what my mother calls me.'

Sarah nodded. 'Why have you got such funny names, you and Miss Grant?'

'My father's mother came from Wales, and we were named after her.'

'I see.'

There was a moment's silence, then Sarah said, 'I'm not bunking school. I've just had hepatitis and I'm not allowed back until the doctor says so.'

'Tough,' said Linnet sympathetically.

But the child's delicate features set in lines of boredom.

'I don't mind. I don't like school. Uncle Stewart says it's because I'm too snooty, but I don't care.'

'Why should you?'

Those uncanny eyes fixed on Linnet's face with interest.

'Well, actually I do mind,' she confided, 'I'd like the other girls to like me, but they're so stupid, and you have to be stupid too for them to like you, and I'm not. Where are you going?'

'Shopping.'

'I'd like to go with you, but Anna won't let me go out. How long will you be?'

Linnet smiled. 'An hour or so, I suppose.'

'I'll probably be dragged inside by then. Can I come to see you in the flat?'

'Yes, if you're allowed.'

'Oh, I'll be allowed.'

As she walked down the street Linnet wondered at the existence of Justin's daughter, astounded that neither Bronwyn nor Stewart had mentioned her. Incredible, she thought, feeling a sudden compassion for the motherless child, who couldn't be much more than eight or nine. Such a pretty child, too, with her pale gold hair and those unusual eyes, as pale as her father's but without the chilling hauteur which hardened his. No doubt she looked like her dead mother with those sensitive features; Linnet found herself hoping rather fervently that Justin didn't dislike her because of it.

She arrived at the flat five minutes after Linnet.

'I saw you from my bedroom window,' she announced, smiling triumphantly. 'You were an hour and a half.'

There followed an enjoyable couple of hours. Sarah must have been starved for conversation, for she chattered and chattered as if Linnet were her own age, revealing an oddly mature mind and an imperious will which, no doubt, was the cause of most of the tension she engendered among her own age group. The easiest way to deal with it, Linnet discovered, was a cool refusal to give in to her demands; when she realised that Linnet had no intention of being dominated she conceded victory gracefully and generously.

Altogether an interesting child.

But Bronwyn dismissed her with a careless remark. 'Spoiled little brat! Justin dislikes her because she reminds him of her mother, so he bends over backwards to give her what she wants. A good boarding school would do her the world of good.'

'She's only a baby,' Linnet protested, appalled at her sister's callousness.

'Old enough to be a damned nuisance,' Bronwyn eyed her, then smiled. 'Remember the sparrow you rescued from the cat and nursed back to health? And the grasshopper which had lost its leg? You cared for it all one summer. You haven't changed. Keep Sarah happy, by all means, if she's taken a fancy to you, but don't let her monopolise you.'

Linnet let the subject lapse, realising that once more she and her sister shared no common ground. But she could not prevent herself from thinking about Sarah, and what Bronwyn had told her made her even more sympathetic towards the child.

So when she appeared the next afternoon, bathing suit over her arm, requesting her company in a swim, Linnet asked merely, 'Does Anna know?'

'Oh yes. She said I wasn't to bother you, but if you wanted to go it would save her from having to watch me.'

Anger spun a small web about Linnet's brain. 'I'll come, then. Just wait while I get into my togs.'

The pool was at the back of the house, carefully planted so that it almost appeared to be a natural feature of the landscape. Surrounded by split sandstone and beds of greenery, with tall tree ferns arching overhead to give shade to the comfortable chairs and loungers, it looked like something out of a very exclusive magazine.

'You go in,' Sarah told her. 'I'll get into my togs in the dressing room. This is the deep end.'

The dressing room or rooms were covered in a gold-flowered creeper; everywhere there were trees and flowers and something discharged a soft, sensuous perfume in the air.

Very easy to get used to, Linnet told herself drily, then dived in. The water was warm, not at all a shock to the system. She swam three lengths before Sarah appeared, her slender little body clad in a bathing suit which emphasised her too obvious bones. Linnet wondered if she was always so thin or whether her illness had reduced her.

She swam well, but tired easily. After ten minutes Linnet climbed out and sat on the edge, pushing her wet hair back from her face.

'Are you getting out so soon?' asked Sarah.

'Yes. This is my first swim of the season, so I'm not going to overdo it.'

Sarah considered her for a few seconds, then made her way to the edge. 'O.K., I'll get out too and keep you company.'

Walled in as the pool was by greenery, it was hot enough to dry their bathing suits almost instantly. After she had covered herself with sunscreen, Linnet made a joke of smothering Sarah in it too, and then led the way to two loungers shaded by a screen of dainty Black-eyed Susan flowers.

'What a funny name!' Sarah was enchanted when her companion mentioned it. 'How do you think they got called that?'

So Linnet made up a story as the sun crawled its slow way westwards and the perfume of the garden bathed them in its sweetness.

'Lovely,' Sarah enthused when she had finished. 'Where did you find that? What book? I'd like to read it.'

'I made it up,' Linnet confessed.

'Gosh!' There was awe in the high voice. 'You *are* clever. Daddy, Linnet made that story up! Isn't she clever?'

Linnet's eyes flew open, met the coldly sardonic gaze of Justin Doyle, and she blushed from her feet to the top of her head, most of it, unfortunately, perfectly obvious because of the scantiness of her bikini.

'Very clever,' he agreed smoothly, lowering himself into a chair beside Sarah's. 'But I thought her name was Eiluned.'

'I can't say that, and anyway, I like Linnet better. She says her mother calls her Linnet.' His daughter chuckled. 'I've got a picture of a linnet in one of my books, but Linnet doesn't look like it.'

'Not in the least,' he agreed, that dispassionate, ironic glance traversing once more the full length of Linnet's body.

She felt as though he had stripped her naked. With a gesture of anger she sprang to her feet, impelled to movement by her humiliation.

'Now that your father's here, I'll go,' she said to Sarah, the words tumbling over themselves in their eagerness to be said.

'Don't go!' The child's face crumpled. 'Daddy, tell Linnet she doesn't have to go just because you're here.'

He stood, took her wrist in a grip which seemed to burn her skin. 'As Sarah says, there's no need to go,' he told her, his glance at once impersonal and bleak.

But she was close to panic. 'I'll have to,' she said rapidly. 'It's time to—to put the dinner on. I'll see you tomorrow, Sarah.'

The grip on her wrist tightened. For one moment she thought that he was going to force her to stay, then he loosed his fingers as though the touch of her was distasteful.

'But, Linnet——'

'Say goodbye, Sarah.'

The sensitive mouth quivered, then firmed. 'Goodbye, Linnet,' she said dully. 'Can we swim again tomorrow?'

'Yes, of course. Goodbye, Sarah. Goodbye, Mr Doyle.'

And she fled, wondering why the man had so unnerved her; aware that she was behaving stupidly, yet quite unable to control that imperative desire to get out of his presence as fast as she could, without caring for dignity.

As she showered, she realised that it was a kind of automatic reaction to danger, a physical need to flee. Fight or flight, she thought. How appropriate!

The flat was hot, almost stuffy in spite of the windows being wide open, so she pulled on shorts and a brief cotton top. It was half past four, she had no idea when Bronwyn was due home, but it would be pleasant to have a meal ready for her.

It took only a few minutes to scrub the new potatoes, make a dressing of yoghurt and mint and vinegar and put it in the fridge, then wash tomatoes and lettuce, slice ham and shell a bag of peas ready for her sister's arrival.

It was while she was doing this that the bell went. She

knew who it would be, and quelled the rising tide of panic within her by taking deep breaths as she washed her hands.

Her hope that Sarah might be with him was dashed.

'May I come in?' he asked, but without fear of a negative answer.

She led the way into the sitting room, turned to face him with defiance, masking the fear she felt.

'What is it?' she asked distantly.

He paused a moment before replying, almost as if he chose his words, and when he spoke it seemed at a tangent. 'Sarah has taken a liking to you.'

Linnet's golden gaze flew upwards. 'I like her, too,' she said when it was obvious that he was waiting for some reply.

'She was upset because she thinks it was my presence which drove you from the pool so abruptly.'

Was there a hint of satire in the deep tones? Almost certainly. Linnet flushed. 'I'm sorry about that,' she said, aware that she was being manoeuvred into some sort of situation—one she knew instinctively, that she was not going to like.

He smiled without humour. 'I doubt it. However, at the moment Sarah needs careful handling. She's been ill, and isn't picking up as quickly as she should. What exactly do you think of her?'

Linnet looked down at her clasped hands, noted with detachment the fluttering of her pulse in a wrist. 'She's a very definite personality—imaginative, forthright, perhaps a little too used to having her own way. I like her.'

The irony in his smile was unmistakable. 'Perhaps,' he suggested blandly, 'a case of diamond cuts diamond.'

'I beg your pardon?'

'You also have a definite personality, you're imaginative, forthright and almost certainly too used to having your own way.'

'Greedy, too, don't forget!' she retorted, angry with him for his patronising words, angry with Bronwyn for putting her in this position and angry with herself as she realised that she would have liked to have his good opinion.

His expression hardened. 'I hadn't forgotten. I doubt if it would be possible for you to make Sarah greedy, so I'm prepared to overlook that—at least as far as she's concerned.'

'Very magnanimous of you!'

He caught at his control, managed to retain it, although a muscle jerked in his jaw and there was a new note of warning in his voice. 'I didn't come here spoiling for a fight, and I refuse to allow myself to be provoked into one.'

'Then what *did* you come for?' she demanded, wishing only to get him out of the place before some precarious part of her control slipped and shattered.

'To ask that for Sarah's sake we appear to be on—at least reasonably friendly terms.'

Linnet stared at him, but before she could say a thing he continued, 'She's still very easily upset; your precipitate departure left her weeping and blaming me. Quite frankly, I wish you'd never met, but as you have and she's taken a fancy to you I'll have to make the best of it. I don't want her to feel that she's being disloyal to either of us when in the other's company, nor do I want her to realise that——'

'That we dislike each other intensely,' Linnet finished drily, as he seemed, probably for the first time in his life, at a loss for words.

He looked at her with something like mockery. 'Is that what it is? Myself, I should have expressed it differently, but you're very young.' He seemed to wait for some answer from her, but when, after a moment, she still remained silent, wondering what on earth he meant, he asked indifferently, 'Have I your assurance, then?'

'What assurance?'

'Your wariness is only exceeded by your deliberate stupidity. Have I your assurance that when Sarah is about you will endeavour to hide this intense dislike, as you call it?'

Instinctively she hunted for the catch in his proposition, turning it over in her mind, seeking for flaws. But it seemed merely the request of a reasonably fond father concerned about the well-being of his daughter.

Grudgingly she answered, 'I see no reason why not.'

'Good. Now will you come over to the house and re-assure her?'

This brought her head up swiftly, her attention arrested by an odd note of triumph in his voice. But there was no sign of it in his expression; the handsome features were set as if in a mask, the hard mouth still a firm line. She concluded she must have been mistaken.

'Very well,' she said reluctantly. 'I'll just go and change.'

'You look perfectly normal in that,' he told her with a chilling lack of interest.

So she went with him, those baseless fears lulled but not completely set at rest.

Sarah was sitting in a small room with the curtains drawn, watching television with an absorption which was obviously faked.

She looked up as Linnet entered the room, scowled, then switched her gaze back to the set.

'She's obviously too busy,' Linnet said to Justin Doyle, and turned to go out.

'No, I'm not.' The child flew across the room, turned the set off, then came slowly towards them, her expression shuttered, as if fearing rejection.

'Have you got your dinner ready?' she asked.

Linnet smiled. 'Yes, apart from the peas.'

'Oh. I think I'm having peas tonight. I hate them.' Sarah said it defiantly.

'Really?' Linnet grinned. 'Ah well, everyone can't like everything.'

Sarah looked puzzled. 'What don't you like?'

'Marrow. Unless it's hidden some way.'

'Daddy, what don't you like?'

Justin answered with barely a hint of amusement, 'Broad beans.'

His daughter gave a crow of laughter. 'I *love* broad beans! How funny! I didn't know you hated them. Linnet, would you like to see my bedroom? I've got lots of books in my bookcase.'

'A clear case of bribery and corruption,' Linnet replied. 'Yes, I'll come, but I must be back home in half an hour.'

'O.K.'

Sarah might have been upset at the tension she sensed, but she showed no signs of it now, dancing down the wide hallway like a sprite, her curls a nimbus of silver above her small earnest face.

She was a good hostess, gravely showing her guest about the large airy room, which had been furnished as a bedsitter for her; it was obvious that she had been accustomed to luxurious surroundings all her life.

'And this is my mother,' she said, pointing out a photograph in a silver frame. 'She died when I was two. Her car went over a bank at the farm.'

Linnet looked compassionately at the wilful, laughing face in the photograph; such a contrast to the grave little girl she had given birth to. And such a contrast to Bronwyn, too. This girl was not a real beauty, her mouth too wide, her nose slightly tiptilted, but she had a radiance which shone through the blacks and greys of the photograph. Her hair was tumbled, far different from Bronwyn's sleek tidiness, and there was an openness about her expression. With Bronwyn you never quite knew what she was thinking. But if Justin was going to marry Bronwyn it must be because she was what he wanted. According to Stewart and Bronwyn this vital girl had had other aspects to her character that the photograph didn't show.

'Daddy doesn't talk about her,' the soft little voice said, not sadly but in resignation. 'P'raps when I'm grown up a bit he'll tell me about her. She looks nice, doesn't she?'

The unconscious pathos caught at the older girl's heart. Giving the child a swift hug, she said, 'She looks lovely, and you look a little bit like her.'

'Do I really? I know I look like Daddy; Anna said that I've got his eyes, but he was brown-haired when he was as old as me. Your hair gets darker when you grow up. Did yours, Linnet?'

'It did, indeed. It was bright carroty red when I was little. Ask Bronwyn, she'll tell you.'

She felt the child's withdrawal as clearly as if it had been physical. 'Miss Grant doesn't like to talk to me,' Sarah said with crisp emphasis, turning away from the lovely, doomed face in the photograph. 'Let's have a look at my books.'

Just before it was time to go Linnet told her a story about Panda Bear she still took to bed with her, then, as Anna had appeared to tell them that it was time for Sarah's bath, she left her in the small bathroom off her bedroom and went back down the hall, her mind still full of Alison Doyle, who had died so tragically seven years ago, and the inferences Stewart Doyle had drawn.

So intent was she that she didn't see the door open as she came up to it, so that Justin's voice beside her brought her from her reverie with a jump.

'I'm sorry I startled you,' he said, not appearing in the least worried.

Linnet looked away swiftly from him; he was too big, too lithely silent for her to be at ease with him even if they had not exchanged insults such a short time ago. Her eyes fell on his hands, holding a book, fine-fingered but strong, and the thought of having anyone's life and happiness in their keeping brought back the panic she had experienced that afternoon.

Without thinking she said in a hard, tight voice,

'Sarah isn't here to see us now, Mr Doyle.'

'Nevertheless, I want to speak to you.'

'Very well.' Capitulating to the inevitable, she preceded him into the room, a study furnished with the same austere luxury as the rest of the house, apart from Sarah's bedroom.

On the wall behind the desk was a painting of hills and coastline, stark, stripped of everything but the lines and colours of the north. It was so impersonal that it repelled, but Linnet could not gainsay its power.

He suffered her to stare for some moments, before saying as collectedly as if she had not been appallingly rude to him,

'Do you like it?'

'Like it? No.' She shook her head. 'But it's fascinating, isn't it?'

'In the correct sense of the word, yes.'

Linnet leaned forward to read the name of the artist, saw a name famous throughout the Pacific and probably well known in Europe by now. Her first ignominious thought was to wonder at the wealth of a man who could buy a painting by such a painter and hang it in his study. Then she shivered, for the terrifying bleakness and power of the painting seemed to symbolise what she knew of Justin Doyle.

'What—what did you want to see me about?' she asked, speaking swiftly, nervously as she turned to face him.

Those strange eyes were shadowed, but he did not appear to be tired; perhaps it was anger, or boredom with someone who had shown herself so lacking in the elementary courtesies.

'I merely wished to tell you that I would be pleased if you could give Sarah as much time as you can spare until you get a job,' he said. 'In fact, if you like, you can consider that a job. I have no idea how you're placed for money——'

'I have enough,' she said, flushing angrily.

'But more than enough is always pleasant.' The cold derision in his tones wounded and condemned.

'For you, perhaps. Not for me. I like your daughter, Mr Doyle, and I'll happily spend time with her, but you don't need to pay me for it.' She met the cool enquiry of his glance, lifted her chin. 'Is that all?'

'That's all.'

'Then I'd better go. Bronwyn may be home.'

He showed her out with the cold courtesy which was

peculiarly his own. Linnet ran across the lawn as if the devils of hell were after her.

CHAPTER THREE

'And how did the interview go?'

Linnet laughed, her vivid face mirroring her emotions in great contrast to the careful deliberation of Bronwyn's countenance.

'Well, I was nervous, of course. It's been a week since I applied and four days since I got the letter back, and believe me, the butterflies were breeding! But she was very nice.'

Delicately demolishing an asparagus spear, Bronwyn waited until it was gone completely before asking, 'What sort of things did she ask?'

'Oh, where I'd worked before. She was a bit shocked when I told her about the boutique, but she rallied.' Frowning in an effort to remember the interviewer's exact words, Linnet laid her fork down. 'She asked me why I wanted to be a librarian, so I said I liked people and loved reading. Then she told me what the job entails—accuracy, and being conscientious. I think my school reports helped. Apparently if I get the place I have to look after the children's section and the club they run for them.'

Bronwyn looked faintly horrified. 'Well, I suppose you'll manage. You certainly can't put a foot wrong as far as young Sarah is concerned. She trails after you like a faithful dog.'

There was nothing disparaging in her sister's voice, but Linnet felt that somehow Bronwyn would never be able to appreciate Sarah. Which would be awful, if she and Justin married.

There was nothing she could say. Her sister was an intensely private person and although she was easy to live with there was no sign of her unbending at all. Certainly, Linnet mused as she washed the dishes, she couldn't ima-

gine the older girl ever needing to confide in anyone. Like
Justin Doyle, she oozed self-sufficiency.

Since that evening when he had offered to pay her for
being a companion to Sarah they had not met, which, she
couldn't help feeling, was a good thing. Even now she
went hot at the remembrance of her rudeness, while
being totally unable to account for it. If Bronwyn hadn't
made up such a story, even if he didn't feel that he had
every reason to distrust and dislike her, Linnet felt that
they still would have felt antipathy for each other.
Mutual incompatibility, no doubt—the opposite to love
at first sight.

Outside it was almost dark; these days of daylight
saving meant that they ate later. The sky had mellowed
into magnificence, the tangerine afterglow of the sunset
giving way to a deep vibrant midnight blue where Venus
glowed like an immense pearl. It was very still and quiet
because of the temporary lull in the traffic, and in the
distance a wayward thrush sang an angelus before retir-
ing to the night.

'By the way,' said Bronwyn, coming into the kitchen
just as Linnet hung up the dishcloth, 'Justin said to tell
you that you can swim in the pool any time you like. You
don't have to wait to go in with Sarah.'

'Kind of him!'

'Yes.' Bronwyn removed the top from the canister of
coffee. 'Mind you, he doesn't mean you to take it literally. Not when he has guests, or when he's there.'

Linnet bit back a sharp retort. Perhaps Bronwyn felt
that she had to dot every i.

'I realise that,' she returned mildly.

'Are you going out with them to the fireworks tomorrow?'

Linnet looked her astonishment. 'The Guy Fawkes display? No!'

'I think you might be,' Bronwyn smiled. 'I know Justin
is taking Sarah, and I'm sure she'll want you to go too.'

She proved right.

'You will come, won't you?' Sarah pleaded the next

day.

'Daddy said you could if you wanted to, and I do want you to, Linnet. You're fun!'

And Daddy isn't? But Linnet didn't ask the question, and although her every instinct rebelled at the idea of going anywhere with Justin Doyle she was not proof against the importunities of his daughter.

'Goody, goody, *goody*!' Sarah chanted, dancing around her, her jean-clad legs long and far too thin. 'Anna is making gingerbread to put in a hamper and we're taking hot drinks, coffee for you and cocoa for me. Oh, Linnet, it will be neat! I wanted to go last year, but I had a cold and we had to stay home and have a little show, which was fun, but this is something else again!'

Justin came down just before Bronwyn arrived home; dressed casually in slacks and a thin polo-necked sweater, for the weather had made one of its abrupt about-turns from hot, summery conditions to a coolness more suited to the late autumn.

'Sarah tells me you're coming with us tonight,' he said as she let him in.

'If that's all right with you.'

He lifted his brows. 'You don't sound terribly enthusiastic.'

Linnet bit her lip. As much as anyone she disliked being made to feel churlish. 'I'm sorry,' she said stiffly. 'Naturally I'm happy to do anything that will make Sarah happy.'

That bored look settled on his features. 'Then I'll pick you up around about half past seven. Make sure that you have something warm to put on in case it gets any colder.'

Why did he have to be so unyielding?

'I'll come up to the house,' she said. 'It's a bit silly for you to have to bring the car down here.'

'Very well, then. I'll see you at seven-thirty.'

And that was that. Bronwyn drove in just as he left, they talked for a few minutes and then she came in, smiling yet with her brows drawn slightly together.

'Told you you'd be going. Young Sarah is like her father in one respect—she knows how to get her own way.'

On an impulse Linnet asked, 'Don't you want to go? I'd be quite happy to stay home.'

'No, thank you. To borrow a cliché, that's not my scene. I like my entertainment to be a little more sophisticated.' She put her bag down on the table, picked up the mail and riffled through it. After a moment she went on, 'Neither do I find young Sarah and me to be exactly compatible.'

'Then what——' Linnet stopped, aware that whatever happened was no business of hers, however much her heart yearned over Sarah.

Her sister shot her an extremely astute glance.

'Don't worry,' she said deliberately, 'I've no intention of being the wicked stepmother. I may not like the child, but I'm not cruel. She's had a pretty tough spin, with that mother and a father who dislikes her yet spoils her. I don't intend to add to her burden.'

If that was meant to be reassuring then it failed. Somehow Linnet felt that Sarah might cope better with an actively cruel stepmother than with an indifferent one. Poor little scrap! And surely her sister was wrong in her summing up of Justin's emotions. He certainly didn't seem to dislike his daughter.

The fireworks were a delight; Sarah laughed and clapped her hands as her eyes grew larger and larger with each fresh enchantment. Even Justin seemed to relax as the evening wore on and they ate gingerbread and drank coffee and the coloured lights flamed and sparkled and whooshed in the amphitheatre.

At last, after the grand finale, a set piece of trees and flowers and birds, Sarah heaved a huge sigh, tucking one hand into Linnet's, the other in her father's.

'That was—*wonderful*,' she murmured with ecstatic emphasis. 'Daddy, can we come again next year?'

'If the weather is fine.'

'And Linnet too?'

Linnet lifted her head at the artless question, met Justin's glance, unfathomable in the semi-darkness.

After a moment the deep tones answered, 'If she wants to come.'

'You will, won't you, Linnet?'

Something odd had happened to Linnet—a kind of internal shudder which set her nerves atingle swept over her, the novelty of it driving coherent thought from her brain.

'You will, won't you?'

Sarah's anxious, insistent voice recalled her to herself, but it took quite an effort to reassure the child. 'If I'm around,' she said cheerfully.

Fortunately, since Sarah did not find this answer to her liking, they caught up with a column of children in wheelchairs, and Sarah was too absorbed in them to continue with her query.

One chair came to a halt. The path was uneven and the girl who pushed was having difficulty manoeuvring the chair past it.

'Carry this, will you?' said Justin, depositing the small hamper in Linnet's hands.

Astounded, she watched as he pushed the wheelchair down the path, said something to the girl who smiled gratefully back at him, and when they reached the footpath and a woman came back to take over, accepted thanks with a smile which made both the handicapped child and the woman flutter before rejoining them.

Another facet of the man. And Linnet saw yet another side to him when, on their way home, he took them to the top of Mount Eden, one of the intriguing little volcanic cones which dot the isthmus of Auckland, scooped Sarah up in his arms and showed them the city spread out below, a spangled map punctuated with the explosions of fire-rockets.

The wide expanse of lights swept up to the Waitakere Hills in the west, across the harbour to the North Shore, a peninsular terminated by Mount Victoria with the dark bulk of Rangitoto Island behind it. The graceful curve of the harbour bridge joining the two shores was lit up, the red warning light at the top clear against the darkness of the sky.

'It looks like a coathanger,' Sarah commented, chuckling from the security of her father's arms. 'I like to see the cars going over it, Daddy. Is that One-Tree Hill, that spiky thing all lit up in the air?'

'Yes, that's the Obelisk. And out to sea is Waiheke Island.'

An imperfectly smothered yawn from his daughter made him say, 'Time to go home, my girl.'

'I'm not tired.'

He laughed at that. It was the first time that Linnet had heard him laugh and she was surprised to discover how warm and pleasant he sounded. Almost like a real human being, she thought frivolously, and no longer wondered at Bronwyn's desire to marry him. Presumably this was a side of him she saw often.

It almost made her regret the fact that Bronwyn had used her as a lever to ensure that she stayed within his orbit. Apart from the unpleasantness of being accused of greed, she didn't like the thought of Sarah's father misjudging her.

And then she reminded herself of the cold Justin Doyle, the hard-as-stone man who had disliked her intensely the minute he had set eyes on her. That man was Sarah's father, too.

But at least Bronwyn was wrong in one thing. He did not dislike his daughter; there was no mistaking the softening of his tones when he spoke to her. And she, astute as she was, would have known if her father merely suffered her. Instead she behaved with him like any normal little girl with her father.

It was a thoughtful Linnet who walked into the flat. It was an obviously ruffled Bronwyn who looked up from the sofa, her expression an odd compound of irritation and amusement, those heavy lids hiding her deepest emotions.

'Have a good time?'

'Yes, great fun. The fireworks were beautiful.'

'Good.' Bronwyn pointed to the table. 'Have some coffee, it's still hot. I've been trying to sober up that stupid Stewart.'

Pouring herself a cup, Linnet asked warily, 'What on earth was he doing here?'

'You might well ask! We hate each other's guts, as he so elegantly put it. Honestly, the man makes me so *mad*!'

And indeed Bronwyn did look furious, her cheeks flushed, her eyes very bright and blue as she forgot her usual elegance of movement and got abruptly to her feet.

'When did he arrive?'

'Oh, about half an hour after you'd gone.'

'And was he drunk?'

Bronwyn gave a snort of anger. 'No, he's never *drunk*. He's always just had a little too much, but it doesn't seem to affect his vicious tongue.' She bit her lip, as though he had hurt her, then went on with an attempt at lightness, 'Oh well, he harms no one but himself. Do you know what he told me? He said the only thing he really wanted to do was farm!'

Linnet looked curiously at her, wondering at the scorn and derision in her voice. 'Well,' she asked reasonably, 'why shouldn't he?'

'Because he's a master of science, that's why! The man has brains, if he cared to use them. If he weren't so weak——' Bronwyn stopped her pacing up and down, darted a swift look at her sister and said crisply, 'You know, I hate waste—and that man is just wasting himself. He works in some menial job for Justin when he could be doing something worthwhile, something that would give him prestige and power.'

'Perhaps he doesn't want prestige and power.'

'Another lame duck? Take my advice, Linnet, don't waste your time trying to help him. I know he's a likeable fool, but he's going to be the one who'll have to pull himself together. No one else can do it for him. He's a kind of parasite; he's sponged on Justin all his life and although he admits he owes him more than he can ever repay he's not prepared to do anything about it. Just ignore him.'

Which sounded very practical and sensible, just like Bronwyn, but apparently even she was unable to prevent herself from trying to help Justin's cousin!

Possibly she didn't want him around, being a parasite, when she married Justin, but somehow Linnet thought it went deeper than that.

Beneath that rather hard exterior it seemed that Bronwyn too suffered from the compulsion to try to help lame ducks. It made Linnet feel that she had things in common with her sister after all.

As she lay in her bed that night, in the floating five minutes before sleep claimed her, she realised that she had not thought of David Perry for at least two days. And when she tried to recapture the pain that her images of his happiness with her mother brought her, it seemed to have faded.

It was there next morning, but in a muted way. Perhaps, she thought wistfully, she was fickle. Certainly her previous boy-friends had never lasted very long, but she had put that down to her increasing maturity. Her love for David had seemed so solid, the pain of his rejection so intense that it was almost tangible; now it was nearly gone, leaving only a memory of his kindness and her own emotional turmoil.

Whatever had happened, whether it had been love or merely the desire for a father figure, as he had termed it, its disappearance made the letter she wrote to her mother much easier. David had indeed smoothed the shock of her departure, for Jennifer's letter had said little about the abruptness of her going, merely chiding her gently for thinking that she could ever be in their way, and hoping that when she had proved her independence she would come back to Sydney to live with them.

Sydney, with its superb beaches and beautiful harbour, its Opera House and bridge, the gay crowds of people made cosmopolitan by immigration—it all seemed so far away, and yet she had left it such a short time ago, measured by sunsets. Something had happened in that time, something she refused to face. Perhaps it was the knowledge that she could be independent.

Two days later, an edgy two days later, she opened a letter which told her that she was to report to the Branch Librarian of the Kent Street Branch for an interview.

'Do you think it means I've got a chance for the job?' she asked Bronwyn breathlessly.

'I'd say so.'

Linnet passed the letter over. 'You read it and tell me what you think.'

After perusing the letter her sister handed it back.

'It means they've made a short list and you're on it. Let's hope the Branch Librarian likes slim redheads with literary aspirations.'

'What will I wear?'

Bronwyn only laughed. 'Nothing too informal. She's probably ninety and unmarried with a nice taste in flat-heeled shoes and horn-rimmed spectacles.'

But the Librarian was in her late twenties, with a wide gold wedding ring and an extremely modern taste in clothes. Her name was Mrs Hayward.

The interview which followed was exhausting, exhaustive and left Linnet feeling as though she had been put through a wringer. Books had been discussed, and there she thought she had held her own, especially when it came to children's books. Some instinct sealed her lips as to her own aspirations there; revelation of that could come later, perhaps. And Mrs Hayward had been very affable at the finish, so it was with a small cautious glow of optimism that Linnet walked the half mile back to the flat.

Sarah was waiting for her, a mutinous expression marring her features. 'Where have you been?' she demanded.

'I've been for an interview.'

'What's that?'

Linnet looked down at her, saw that she was genuinely upset and ran a tender hand over her pale head.

'I've been to see a lady, the Librarian at Kent Street,

to see if I'm suitable to work in her library.'

'Work in the library?'

'Yes.' After pouring out glasses of tangelo juice Linnet led the way to the little table in the kitchen. 'If I go to work there you can join the Library Club. I'll be in charge of that. It meets twice a month and does all sorts of interesting things.'

'Like what?'

'Oh, book reviews, and handcrafts—all sorts. Would you like that?'

Sarah set her barely touched drink down. 'Yes,' she said mutedly, 'but if you go to work you'll be away all day and I won't see you.'

'Oh, you'll see me. Not as much, of course, but I won't lose sight of you.'

This was one aspect of the business Linnet had not thought of. Fortunately Sarah didn't seem disposed to take it any further, though she was a little subdued for the rest of the afternoon.

But at seven-thirty that evening the telephone went; Bronwyn answered, nodded a couple of times, then hung up.

'They want you up at the house,' she said crisply. 'Sarah is having a tantrum and won't go to bed until you're there.'

So Linnet ran up to the house, her forehead creased into a frown.

Justin was in the bedroom, stroking the child's hot forehead, but he stood when Anna led Linnet into the room and moved aside. He looked very angry; somehow Linnet knew that his anger was directed not at the child but at her. Nobody could possibly be angry with the small heap of grief in the bed.

'Sarah,' she said tentatively, 'Sarah, it's me.'

A hot little hand squirmed out from under the covers, grasped hers and held on tight.

'That's a shocking noise,' Linnet said calmly. 'Have you given yourself a headache yet?'

There was a gulp, a muffled, 'No,' and the sobbing eased slightly.

'Well, you're about to give me one,' Linnet went on. 'What disaster has occurred?'

Sarah loved big words. The weeping ceased, except for the involuntary whoop that comes after prolonged sobbing.

'Better blow your nose,' Linnet said matter-of-factly. 'Here, here's my hankie.'

Sarah blew, handed it back and emerged, flushed, tragic-eyed, her sensitive mouth trembling. 'I don't want you to go to w-work!' she whispered. 'I don't want you to be away. The days are so long and you make me laugh. I want you to stay with me.'

Forgetful of the presence behind her, Linnet bent forward and took the mutely pleading little face between both hands, kissing each flushed cheek.

'My poor darling, you *have* got yourself into a tizz,' she said tenderly. 'Now, I'm going to tell you a story, and when I come to the end of it you'll be asleep.'

'But you won't go away, will you?'

'No, I won't go away.' It was a reckless promise, but one that Linnet had every intention of keeping. Only later did she realise how inextricably the child was entwined in her heartstrings.

It took only five minutes of low talking before Sarah was asleep. Releasing the now cool little hand, Linnet stood up, surprised to see that Justin Doyle was still there.

In silence she preceded him out into the hall; it came as no surprise when he said quietly, 'I want to talk to you,' and opened the door into his study.

Her eyes flew to the painting, but she looked at it for only a few moments before turning to face him, her hands clasped behind her back as she braced herself to meet an onslaught.

He surprised her by saying, 'Sit down, Linnet,' as he gestured towards a chair.

Gingerly she perched herself on the very edge, watching him from beneath lowered lashes. He looked tired, the magnificent virility dimmed, but there was no diminishing of the cold command of the man.

'Now perhaps you can tell me what all that was about,' he said as he leant against the desk.

So she told him.

When she had finished he was silent, his eyes fixed on her face with a regard as intent as it was impersonal.

Uneasy beneath the concentrated impact she moved restlessly, lowered her gaze, clasped her hands together in her lap and wished he would say something.

'I realised she'd taken a violent fancy to you,' he said at last, just before she screamed, 'but I hadn't realised it went so deep.'

'I hadn't either. It's because she hasn't any playmates.'

He shrugged. 'Possibly. It could as easily be because she has no mother. Whatever the reason, she has apparently given her heart to you. I've never seen her so distraught.'

Which made her feel guilty. 'I'm sorry,' she said, wishing fervently that the child hadn't the ability to tug so violently at her heartstrings.

Surprisingly Justin smiled, bleakly it was true, but it did warm the coldness of his expression. 'It's hardly your fault,' he stated drily. 'Tell me, have you set your heart on becoming a librarian?'

'I want to very much,' she said, half aware of what he was going to offer.

'If I offered you a position as Sarah's companion would that change your mind at all?'

Incredible how strongly she reacted! 'No,' she answered swiftly. 'I'm sorry—I'm very fond of Sarah, but I can't—I—well——' she finished lamely, 'I do want to be a librarian.'

'And if you don't get the job?'

'I'd look for another,' she replied in a low voice, aware only of an intense aversion to his idea.

'I see.'

Her attention caught by the note of anger in his voice she looked up and saw the man of that first interview, icy with contempt because she did not measure up to his standards.

Or was it just that? Somehow Linnet felt that her own swift denial of his offer and the anger it aroused were part of something much more than his desire to see his daughter happy. It was almost as though he was attacking her independence, her desire to lead at last a life of her own, to be free. But surely—swiftly she dismissed the idea. It was too ridiculous. All that she had to deal with was a naturally autocratic man who was prepared to ride roughshod over anyone—perhaps, she guessed, to ease a conscience which might be a little tender, for if Sarah had been a happy child she would not have developed this desperate attachment.

The thought of Sarah weakened her resolve far more than the father's anger, but supported by the deep instinctive conviction that if she gave in she would be sacrificing far more than any career as a librarian she said once more, quite clearly, 'No. I wish I could—but you must see that it's unfair to ask.'

'I see a woman who selfishly puts her own desires ahead of a child's,' he returned harshly.

'That's not so!' She jumped to her feet, anger roused by the blatant unfairness of his comment. Without stopping to think she positioned herself in front of him, her face irradiated by her emotions. 'I've seen no indication that you put your needs or desires in second place to Sarah's,' she stated angrily. 'Why expect me to?'

'You allowed her to become fond of you.'

'Oh, for heaven's sake! The child is desperate for someone to care! Someone who'll listen to her and talk to her and be interested in her—she couldn't help becoming attached to the first person who showed any interest.'

Something in his very stillness warned her that she had trespassed on an area that was very sensitive, but she was too angry to care. Pushing her fingers through her hair as though it was his face she would like to rake with her nails, she continued wearily, 'She's also highly strung and too indulged. She's not too young to learn that she can't always have her own way, or that emotional blackmail doesn't work. Where on earth did she learn to do that?'

'It must be born in her,' he said bitterly. 'God knows, her mother was an expert.'

Linnet's eyes flew to meet his, saw in their pale depths a bleak anger that wrung her heart.

'You tried some of it yourself,' she said, more gently. 'I'm sorry, Justin, but I'm not going to give in to either Sarah's or yours.'

'You promised her that you'd stay.'

She bit her lip, remembering that impulsive remark.

'Yes. Well, I meant it. If I get this job, I'll want board fairly close, so I'll be able to see quite a bit of her.'

'Don't be ridiculous!' At her startled glance he went on impatiently, 'There's no need for you to go at all.'

'I said that I have no intention of sponging on Bronwyn, and believe me, I meant it.'

The wide shoulders moved in a shrug, dismissing her defiant statement.

'She won't be there for much longer. When she's gone you may have the flat. Anna's quite happy with her quarters here.'

Linnet felt as though someone had kicked her in the solar plexus. Fixing her eyes on the collar of his shirt, she sought for words, finally found them. 'I'm sorry that I implied you didn't care for Sarah,' she said tonelessly. 'I can see that you must love her very much if you're prepared to have me about the place.'

Again those shoulders moved, very slightly. With a drawl which was at variance with the normal clipped precision of his speech, he retorted, 'Perhaps I just want her to be happy.'

Again her glance sped upwards, saw the mockery glinting in the depths of his eyes and the irony of his smile. Without volition she stepped backwards, impelled by that instinct inborn in all women which recognises danger.

The mockery intensified, rendering him extremely attractive and very dangerous. He didn't move, not a muscle, but she felt that he was willing her to come to him; she could feel the aura of his masculinity holding her captive.

Physical attraction, said her brain, keeping her body still with immense concentration. It was as potent as a spell, and he was deliberately and unscrupulously using it.

With an effort of will which exhausted her she turned away, saying as calmly as she could over her wildly beating heart,

'Possibly. I'm not particularly interested in your reasons, but I can promise that I won't deliberately hurt Sarah.'

'Thank you.' His voice was cold and deep, without emotion.

But Linnet didn't dare look at him all the way back to the flat—several miles, it seemed in the scented darkness—and when they got there she fled inside feeling that she had narrowly escaped from a danger all the more severe because it was indescribable.

Bronwyn emerged from the bathroom some ten minutes later clad in a negligee as pretty as it was impractical, all satins and laces which complimented her petite beauty.

'From the shop,' she said complacently when Linnet admired it. Then after one of her devastatingly shrewd glances, 'You look as though you've been interrogated by experts. Sarah acting up?'

'Yes.' Linnet told her what had happened, omitting, for some obscure reason, Justin's offer of a job and her own reaction to it. Also she did not tell her what Justin had said about Bronwyn not needing the flat for much longer.

'I told you she was a spoilt little piece,' her sister commented. 'I feel sorry for her when she's not around, but I must confess her presence irritates me. Anyway, you can stay here. There's no reason for you to find board.'

It was hardly an enthusiastic offer, but that it had been made at all surprised Linnet. 'I didn't intend to park myself on you for good and all,' she protested.

Bronwyn grinned. 'I know. But it suits me to have you here. You can keep Sarah happy, and by the time she's

old enough to go to boarding school you'll be old enough
to get married.'

'I doubt if she'll ever like boarding school,' Linnet said
doubtfully, remembering the sensitive features, the passionate grief of the child.

Bronwyn dismissed this. 'She'll get used to it, like all of
us. You didn't go, did you? I did. You're horribly home-
sick for six months and then you love it.'

'Well, I hope so.'

'You think I'm hard, don't you? No, you don't need to
prevaricate. I can see it written large all over your face.'
Collapsing gracefully into a chair, the older girl put her
feet on the arm of the sofa and surveyed them intently,
her emotions hidden by the heavy lids of her eyes. After a
moment she said levelly, 'You can have no idea of the
sort of life I led as a child. My mother died when I was
five and within a year Dad had married Jennifer, and a
year after that you were born. Your mother was as kind
to me as she could be, but we fought a battle for Dad's
affection. It was as fierce as it was hidden, but we both
knew that only one could win.' She looked up at Linnet,
her blue gaze very cool. 'Well, I won, but even then, she
won. She took you and left and Dad retired into a kind of
half life, behind a wall where I couldn't reach him.'

Linnet couldn't prevent a small sound of protest.
'There's no need for you to tell me all this, Bronwyn.'

'My dear girl, I'm not baring my soul for my own
pleasure. I'm explaining to you exactly why I'm the way
I am.' She smiled without humour. 'You see, you were
the one thing I loved then; I was very proud of you. It
must have been fairly deep rooted, because I've discovered that I care for your good opinion.' Without
giving Linnet time to reply she continued, 'Well, that sort
of childhood helps you to use your brain to plan ahead. I
determined that I was going to become independent as
soon as possible, so with Dad's help I bought the boutique and discovered that I was a pretty good business
woman. It's a success, and that's important to me. That's
why Justin and I get on so well together—we have the

same need for success, and neither of us need or want the kind of romantic attachment I'm sure you'll be happiest with. Love conquers all, that sort of thing. For you it might work—for me, never.'

'How do you know?' Linnet asked soberly. 'Perhaps you've just never experienced it.'

Her sister smiled cynically. 'Oh yes, I have, and was miserable. To lose control—well, there's no need to rake over the details. I hated it. I know what I'm doing, Eiluned, what's right for me. If I seem hard—well, that's the penalty I'll have to pay for thinking things through and refusing to be ruled by my emotions. But I don't want to seem unkind. Sarah will be quite safe with me.'

Linnet realised that she really believed this; it seemed that any effort to convince Bronwyn that there were many ways to be unkind to a sensitive child other than the deliberate would be doomed to failure. Perhaps, she thought wearily, aware that she was evading the issue, perhaps by being around Sarah Bronwyn would learn how to manage her and make her happy.

Later that evening, as she brushed her hair before sleeping, she wondered why Justin's blunt announcement that Bronwyn would not need the flat for much longer had affected her so strongly. It was tantamount to saying that their marriage was fairly close; the reason she felt so concerned about that was that she worried about Sarah, of course. An odd thing, the maternal instinct. For Sarah's sake she wished rather fervently that Bronwyn would develop it.

The child arrived immediately after breakfast the next day, half apologetic, half defiant, but when Linnet treated the incident with casual unconcern she dropped her uneasy belligerence and followed suit.

'I'm sorry,' she said, squeezing her companion's hand, 'but I couldn't sleep, and I got to thinking about you, and I just got all silly and upset. Linnet, did you mean it when you said you wouldn't go?'

'Yes. Bronwyn has agreed that I can stay here with her.'

As always when the older girl's name was mentioned, Sarah's expressive countenance registered sullen resignation. But after a moment she said, 'That's nice. When will you know if you've got your job?'

'In a week or so.'

'Good; then we've got a week together.' She was jubilant, making suggestions about ways to spend the week, some ridiculous, some interesting. Then a strange expression crossed her face; she chuckled suddenly, but when Linnet asked her what was up she shook her head, smiling mysteriously.

'Wait and see,' she teased. 'Linnet, do you want to write?'

Bemused by this sudden change of attitude, for Sarah had always seemed a little jealous of her writing, she said, 'Yes, I do.'

'Then you sit down and write,' Sarah told her graciously. 'I'll just pop up to the house.'

Once writing time was forgotten; it was late in the afternoon when she surfaced, hungry, thirsty and surprised at being left alone for so long.

Sarah had still not appeared when Bronwyn came home, but within a few minutes she was down and with her came her father, looking distinctly grim and unapproachable in the warm spring sunlight.

'What on earth——?' Bronwyn looked startled, but there was no sign of it when she opened the door to Justin and his daughter.

Like a coward Linnet stayed in the kitchen where she supervised dinner, but Sarah said imperiously, 'Come on, Linnet, we need you too.'

Once in the sitting room Justin refused Bronwyn's offer of a drink and began, 'Sarah tells me that you have a week in hand before you know about this library job. Is that so?'

For all the world as if she was a recalcitrant pupil and he a stern headmaster. Stifling the desire to answer pertly, Linnet said, 'Yes, about a week.'

He nodded, 'In that case, would you like to go with

Sarah to our house on Kawau Island, up the Gulf?' Momentarily his glance rested on the small silver head of his daughter, then flicked across to catch and hold Linnet's. 'She thinks—and I agree—that a week in the sun will benefit her. Anna is too busy to take her. If you agree I'll be very grateful.'

Sarah must have been warned against being importunate, but those pale eyes so like her father's grew enormous with the strain of staying silent.

Linnet dithered. She wanted to go—Auckland had suddenly become stifling to her—but the thought of being beholden in any way to Justin was galling.

Then Bronwyn said, amusement colouring her words, 'Of course she'll go, Justin. She's dying to say yes.'

'Linnet?'

She nodded. At once Sarah squealed with delight, flung her arms around her father's waist and hugged him hard, then danced across the room and fastened herself on to Linnet's hand.

'I knew you would,' she stated with enormous contentment.

CHAPTER FOUR

THEY left from Mechanic's Bay in the heart of Auckland, flying in a seaplane which took the three of them—for Justin accompanied them—and the pilot, but only just.

It was, Linnet decided, quite the smallest seaplane in the world. As her only previous experience of flight had been in the enormous jets which spanned the Tasman Sea—and they terrified her—she was convinced that she was going to be dead of fright before they reached the island.

But the pilot seemed quite happy, Sarah was ecstatic and Justin—well, it would be a very foolhardy plane which would let Justin Doyle down!

He was sitting now between them both, so that they could see through the windows. The warmth and hardness of his arm was against her shoulder, and she was acutely aware of the faint masculine scent of him. Something close to a panic drove her to peer intently out of the window at the enormous oil tanks on the shore.

'We're away!' the pilot shouted, and the note of the engines changed as the plane surged across the quiet waters of the bay. Within a few seconds another change in the engine noise revealed that they were airborne.

Linnet forgot the size of the plane, forgot everything but the beauty of the scene below, the harbour glinting and sparkling in the sun, the islands spread like emeralds of differing shades scattered across the water and the darker, deeper colour of the outer Gulf sheltered by the length of Great Barrier Island and the Coromandel Peninsular from the limitless Pacific Ocean.

A ship made its way up the channel between the North Shore and the sombre bulk of Rangitoto Island, the most recent volcano in all of that volcanic area.

'It's only dormant, like all of the others,' Justin said

into her ear. 'It erupted about nine hundred years ago. That's weathered lava, the dark rock it's composed of.'

She nodded, conscious that he had bent closer to her in order to make himself heard above the plane's engines. It was a relief when Sarah claimed his attention.

In all too short a time the shape of Kawau Island, almost bisected by Bon Accord harbour, appeared, the white coves and beaches glistening in the sun.

'Nearly there,' the pilot informed them unnecessarily over his shoulder. 'Seat belts tight? O.K., then down we go.'

They landed on the calm waters of the harbour, taxied across to a bay protected from the south by a small promontory covered in pines. About half way down was a wharf, long and slender, from which a launch was leaving.

'There's Mr McCarthy,' Sarah shrilled. 'Look, Linnet, there's the house!'

'Where?'

Laughing, over-excited, Sarah leaned across her father and grabbed Linnet's hands just as she freed herself from her safety belt. Giving them an enormous tug, she half hauled Linnet across Justin's lap, so that she was sprawled rather inelegantly over his knees, her head against his shoulder. Beneath her ear she could hear the muted thunder of his heart. Then, with a grip which was far from gentle, he set her back in her place and began to scold Sarah for her impetuosity.

'I'm sorry,' said Sarah, laughing. 'You should have seen your face, Linnet! You looked as if Daddy was a *shark* or something!'

'Hardly,' Linnet protested, acutely conscious of hair dishevelled by contact with his shoulder.

'Oh, yes, you did. And Daddy looked shocked!'

Justin lifted his brows at his unrepentant daughter, but the anger had gone from his expression, to be replaced by wry amusement. 'You're an imaginative child,' he said mildly. 'Come on now, here's Mr McCarthy.'

Who turned out to be a tall, bearded young man, clad

in shorts and nothing else, who received Sarah's greeting
with a gentle smile, helped Linnet into the launch and
took the suitcases as the pilot passed them out, talking
quietly to Justin as he stowed them below in the cabin.

They looked an oddly incongruous pair, Justin in trousers and shirt which, although casual, were beautifully cut,
and the extremely casual, very tanned young man who
must be the caretaker, but it was quite apparent that they
were friends. Reluctantly once more Linnet had to revise
her opinion of Justin. He could not be as stuffily superior
as she had thought him if he had found friendship with
Mr McCarthy.

'There's the house,' said Sarah, all at once very quiet.
'See, Linnet?'

And this time Linnet saw it, a long building of stained
wood, inconspicuous against the wooded hillsides of the
promontory, surrounded by greenery. Unconsciously she
sighed, caught by the beauty of the scene, the rightness of
the house in its old, sleepy setting.

Then the launch nosed up against the wharf, and
Sarah was dragging at her hand, her moments of quiet-
ness gone. 'Come *on*, Linnet! Let's go up and see Cherry.'

'No, we'll help with the luggage first.'

But Justin said from behind, 'You go on ahead, Rob
and I will bring up the bags.'

Their feet made a satisfactory slap, slap along the tim-
bers of the wharf, a sound which changed to a crunch as
they came off on to a path of broken shells worn smooth
and round by the sea. The spicy, aromatic scent of
manuka was strengthened by the balsam of the pines and
along the white beach a pohutukawa leaned out across
the water, its first flowers dark scarlet amongst the green
and silver of the foliage.

It was very quiet. The sea-plane had taken off while
they were in the launch and was now a faint hum on the
edge of hearing. There was no other sound but the soft
hush of the waves against the huge wooden piles of the
wharf. Even Sarah was silent, her expression absorbed in
a kind of near-ecstasy.

Then, as if on cue, a dog barked, at first up by the house, but it came closer rapidly.

'It's all right, it's only Goori,' Sarah explained kindly. 'He sounds fierce, but he's really gentle as a lamb.'

The oddly named Goori was an enormous creature, part German shepherd, part Labrador, Linnet guessed, and another part which was plain mongrel. He looked as though he ate babies for breakfast, but his tail wagged hard enough to belie his appearance, and when Sarah introduced Linnet he sniffed her proffered hand delicately before giving it an enthusiastic lick.

'There, he knows you,' Sarah said happily.

From behind her father added, a note of mockery in his voice, 'Theoretically he's a watchdog—or so Rob assures me.'

And Rob McCarthy laughed. 'Of course he's a watchdog. He barks, even if he doesn't attack. Nobody gets far on to Goori's patch without him letting us know.'

All very chummy, Linnet decided as she and the child preceded them up the narrow path towards the house. Justin Doyle was a complex man with many sides to his character; it might pay to remember that she didn't know him very well.

The house was another surprise. It was not new, being at least forty years old, built in the days when beach houses had not yet become a status symbol. But it was comfortable, stylish in its very simplicity and well cared for.

Cherry McCarthy was a large-boned woman, younger than Rob with enormous brown eyes, a wicked smile and her husband's bone-deep suntan. She too greeted Justin with pleasure, quite unmixed with awe, smiled the smile of an old friend at Sarah, and was introduced to Linnet. Her expression was interested but not curious; she was not the curious type. Even if she had been she would have learned little, for Justin did not say anything about Bronwyn being her sister. He did, however, tell Cherry that he would be leaving early the next morning, which was a relief. Ever since the seaplane had left them Linnet had wondered how long he intended to stay.

It was a very quiet day. The rest of the morning was spent being shown over the property by Sarah while Justin was closeted in an office with Rob, then came a swim before lunch and the meal itself, eaten on the beach beneath the umbrella of the pohutukawas.

After lunch Sarah went to sleep in a lounger, Justin retired to the house, and Linnet followed Sarah's example, lulled to rest by the quiet warmth of the air. It was as though all of the traumas of the past weeks had caught up with her at once, from her mother's wedding to the battles she had had with Justin, and the fact that she hadn't slept very well the night before, no doubt because she wasn't accustomed to being hustled as Justin had hustled her.

Scarcely had she agreed to go with Sarah than he had stated that there was no reason why they shouldn't leave the next day. Half an hour after he and Sarah had left to go back to the big house he had rung to tell her that all was arranged.

'When Justin wants things done, they get done,' Bronwyn had said, almost proudly.

She never spoke a truer word.

The impatient 'pink-pink' of some small bird woke her. A swift glance at her watch revealed that she had slept for an hour or so. Sarah was still asleep, sprawled with the unconscious grace of childhood on the lounger, one small hand clenched beneath her chin. A kind of yearning clutched at Linnet's heart; the child was so vulnerable in her innocence and youth. She wished she could keep her from all pain and grief, even as the sensible part of her brain told her that pain and grief were two of the things which helped any character to mature.

Some instinct told her that she was being watched. Very slowly she moved her head, met Justin Doyle's sardonic glance and felt the tell-tale heat of a blush across her skin.

He was sitting on the overhanging limb of the tree, one leg dangling, his elbow on the other knee, his hand supporting his chin. Clad in shorts and a tee-shirt he looked very much younger than the Justin Doyle she knew, and rather more approachable.

'How long have you been there?' she blurted, because it was obvious he wasn't going to talk, and she couldn't think of anything else to say.

'About ten minutes.'

She disliked the thought of him watching her as she slept, and said so.

'Yet you were watching Sarah.'

'I didn't say it was logical,' she returned crossly, 'I just don't like it.'

He chuckled at that and swung himself down from the tree to sit in the deckchair beside her. 'Because you feel unprotected?'

'Yes, I suppose so.'

'Asleep you look scarcely older than Sarah. But then—' with a measuring glance down the length of her body—'even awake you don't look much older than Sarah.'

For some reason this calm dismissal irritated her. Although she knew it would be wiser to say nothing she couldn't prevent herself from retorting, 'Don't forget I'm old enough to be——' the word greedy hovered on her tongue.

'Don't say it.' Incredibly he leaned over and put his finger over her lips.

Linnet's eyes widened to their fullest extent; after the first second her mouth stopped movement, but during that second it felt as though she had kissed his finger.

'Let's call a truce, shall we?' Justin removed his hand, smiled full into her astonished face. 'It's too hot to be angry, so don't pick another fight with me.'

'I don't pick fights.' But she was too bemused to be able to infuse her voice with the right amount of defiance.

And he smiled again. 'There, you're trying it now.'

When Justin Doyle smiled like that, his already potent attraction became overwhelming. Linnet found it hard to believe that the man beside her was really the icy tyrant she had met in Auckland; her last lingering queries as to why Bronwyn wanted to marry him were swept away.

But she couldn't just sit and stare at him, or he'd think she was mad. With an effort she replied, 'No, I'm not trying to—pick a fight, I mean. And I think a truce is a good idea. I don't *like* quarrelling.'

He laughed at that, a soft sound which had something of satisfaction in it. 'You could have fooled me, but I'll believe you. Now, tell me why you're so determined to be a librarian.'

He really wanted to know, so she told him. 'Because I love books. Not just reading them—I love the look of them and the feel of them, the smell of them when you open a new one, and the funny musty smell that catches your breath when you open a really old one. I can spend hours in bookshops, and I love talking about them.' She smiled, aware that those penetrating eyes were fixed on her. 'And I love reading them too, of course. And I like people. And you have to add to that what my mother calls an insatiable desire to know.'

He lifted his brows at that. 'To know what?'

'Everything.' She gestured largely at the horizon. 'For instance, what's that we can see? That chunk of land?'

'That's the mainland. Those two islands are Pine and Rabbit Islands.'

'And that double-peaked hill on the skyline?'

'Tamahu.'

'How high is it?'

He laughed at that. 'I see what you mean. Do you like maps?'

'Oh, yes, very much.'

'I'll show you one of the area later, when Sarah wakes, then you'll be able to work out exactly where you are—and how high everything is!'

A small boat tore across the harbour, distance muting the high-pitched whine of the motor. Overhead two sea-gulls circled slowly in the sun, while kahawai birds followed a shoal of the tiny fish they fed on, and a man in a dinghy up-anchored and rowed carefully towards the opposite shore, the creak of the rowlocks resounding across the bay.

Justin asked, 'If you wanted to marry, what would happen to the desire to become a librarian?'

Instantly her thoughts flew to David, and to her surprise she felt nothing, only a profound relief that he had had the tact and compassion to save her from making a fool of herself.

'Most women work until they want a family,' she answered dreamily, immensely relieved at her heart-free condition.

'If there was no need to?'

She laughed. 'Very few men can afford to keep an idle wife nowadays! Anyway, I think that I'd still like to work so that I had some qualifications.'

'Sarah tells me you write.'

'Oh!' She sat up, then forced herself to relax back into the lounger. 'Well, yes,' she said warily, 'but I haven't had anything published yet.'

'If you had, would you give up outside work?'

She pondered. 'I don't know. Yes, I think so. I'm a compulsive writer, even if it's not very good. If anything else got in the way of it, I'd probably dump it to write, I think.' Then she went on, 'I started when I was five or so, and I've always kept it up—I feel bereft if I haven't got a project going.'

It was oddly easy to talk about her writing. Normally she hated discussing it, but Justin seemed genuinely interested; he certainly wasn't patronising, as some people were inclined to be.

'And what standard do you think you've reached?'

Linnet sighed. 'I don't know. Sometimes I think it's good and I get excited, and then I decide it's absolute rubbish. I'll have to leave it to the publisher to decide.'

'But you wouldn't be writing if you didn't think it was worth publishing.'

Linnet looked at him with surprise and respect. 'True,' she said ruefully, 'but quite often when I re-read something after it's corrected I think it's rubbish.'

'I'd say you've reached the stage where it's impossible for you to be objective. The only thing to do is to get something off and get an impartial opinion.'

'Well, that's rather encouraging.' She wriggled rather uneasily in her chair. For some reason she didn't want to find Justin too approachable; things had been simpler when she could dislike him enthusiastically.

And her writing was too personal for her to be able to discuss it at any length. Fortunately he seemed to realise this, or perhaps he was just bored with a subject which could really be of very little interest to him, for he began to talk about a play which had been brought by an overseas company to Auckland. It was one she had seen in Sydney, so she was able to hold her own in the ensuing conversation.

Later, as they swam, she scolded herself for being surprised at his interest in theatre. That house in Auckland proved that he was no hard-headed business man with a nose for nothing but profits, so she should not have been surprised at his intelligent and hard-hitting comments. She rather thought that he had been a little startled by her, too. And she grinned rather complacently at a piece of seaweed floating by. It would be good for him to learn that someone of her age wasn't interested only in pop singers!

When the evening cooled down, they sat in the shade of a wide terrace roofed by a pergola almost smothered in heavily scented white mandevillea flowers; Linnet and Sarah played Chinese Checkers, and then Sarah coaxed her father into a game of chess while Linnet read. Not for long, however, as Sarah decided that she needed help and with a return of her imperious manner demanded her presence.

'I can't play chess,' she protested.

'Can't play? Daddy, Linnet can't play chess!' Sarah was clearly appalled at such ignorance.

'Then we'd better teach her, hadn't we?'

Of the two of them Justin was by far the better teacher, Linnet discovered. Surprisingly he had reserves of patience when he cared to use them, and a clear way of explaining things which helped her considerably.

Sarah thoroughly demoralised her by pushing back a bishop after what she considered to be a well-thought-out move and saying gently, 'Now, Linnet, just think hard! Daddy and I won't mind if you try again, will we, Daddy?'

Linnet looked up, caught Justin's eye and began to laugh. After a moment he joined her and then Sarah, quite unable to see any joke, but not wishing to be left out.

'Dinner's ready!'

Cherry's gay voice broke up the chess party. She didn't ask what the joke was, but Sarah told her anyway on the way to the dining room and was rewarded by her laughter too.

Somehow the incident set the seal for the evening. They dined alone, the three of them, Sarah in a mad mood which lit up her eyes and coloured her expressive little face rosy with excitement.

Linnet was intrigued by the relationship between her companions. She had heard of small girls who flirted with their fathers, but Sarah did not do that. And she could not imagine Justin responding to a flirtatious attitude from anyone; he was too aware of his dignity for that. But Sarah definitely sparkled when she had his attention, and he paid her the compliment of responding as if she were an adult, while never forgetting that she was a child.

Intriguing, definitely. Unbidden came the thought that if Bronwyn were here the delicate balance of personalities would be upset. Naturally, for Bronwyn would expect— and receive—a considerable amount of Justin's attention for herself as a desirable woman. It was only because Justin did not see Linnet in that light that she was able to see father and daughter as they really were.

Pensively demolishing a bowl of delicious strawberries and cream, she was startled to find herself feeling wistful, and wondered crossly why.

Then Justin smiled at her. 'You look rather triste. Is

the meal not to your liking?'

'The meal,' she returned with deep conviction, 'is superb. I can see I shall have to ask Mrs MacCarthy to give me lessons.'

'Me too.' Sarah looked enthralled at the prospect.

'I'm sure she will, if you ask politely.' He smiled down at his daughter. 'Finished?'

'Yes, thank you.'

'Then let's go. It must be very close to your bedtime.'

Sarah wailed at this, but he was inexorable, and within half an hour she was in bed, storied, kissed and tucked in.

And that left Linnet alone with him in the big living room with its quarry tiled floor and great banks of indoor plants. At once the room seemed far too small. Restlessly she wandered over to a cane whatnot piled high with African violets, the flowers in all shades of amethyst and blue and white, wine-coloured and pink, held on slender stalks above their dark velvety leaves.

They had dined late, but as it was summer time the sun had only just sunk behind the pine-clad hill to the west of the bay, and it was still quite light.

'Would you like the television on?' His voice was remote, yet there was a note of irony in it.

For a moment she was tempted. At least the television was impersonal. Unfortunately she was almost certain that she hated the programmes on both channels at this time.

So she said, 'No, thank you. Not unless you want to.'

'Not tonight.'

Silence. A rustle of paper made her peep sideways. Yes, he was reading the newspaper. Obviously bored to death. It was a blow to the ego, of course, but she hadn't been hired to keep him entertained, so why get so uptight?

Restlessly she moved across to the wide, sliding glass doors out on to the terrace. On the lawn below a harassed female blackbird hopped here and there, chased by her large and pugnacious offspring demanding with angry 'quink-quink' the worm she had in her beak. After a minute or so she turned, stuffed the worm down its

throat, then hopped off, her sleek form expressing outraged huffiness.

Linnet chuckled. The newspaper rustled behind her,
but no other sound came. Slowly, so as not to disturb the
birds on the lawn, she stepped out on to the terrace. The
sky was that peculiar washed-out blue which marked the
approach of twilight, but there was not a cloud to be
seen. Tomorrow would be another hot day. The air was
absolutely still, so still that the harbour and the sea
beyond it looked like a sheet of steel, silver-grey and
smooth as glass. Soon the sky would darken and the moon
would rise . . .

'Full moon tonight. It's always a magnificent sight
over the harbour.'

Heavens, but he moved as quietly as a beast of prey!
Linnet managed to prevent the nervous jump his voice
had aroused in her, but her voice was uneven as she replied.

'I can imagine it. This is a beautiful spot, Justin—like
paradise.'

'It's very quiet at this time of the year, of course. In the
summer there's considerably more activity.'

'Oh, I like it the way it is now.' She leaned against the
upright, keeping her voice soft so as not to disturb the
birds. 'It's so peaceful.'

'More than it used to be, now that the hotel licence has
been taken from Governor Sir George Gray's Mansion
House and it's been restored. Have you been there?'

The air flowed softly over her hot cheekbones as she
shook her head. 'No. I've seen photographs, of course.'

Everyone had. The Mansion House had been the
refuge of that complex, interesting man of the last century, who had set down his version of many Maori myths
and legends, governed New Zealand, returned as Prime
Minister and lived like a lord in his sub-tropical bay at
the mouth of the harbour.

'If you're interested get Rob to take you there. Or you
can walk up the hill and go by the track. It's a pleasant
walk along the old coach road, the only road on the

island. It was Governor Gray who liberated wallabies and kookaburras on the island.'

Linnet turned a dazzled face to him. 'Truly? Are there any left?'

'Oh yes.' He sounded a trifle grim. 'That's why this peninsula is fenced off with deer-proof netting. Otherwise there wouldn't be anywhere near so many trees and shrubs in the garden. They're destructive little beasts.'

'Do you ever see them?'

'In the twilight, occasionally,' He looked around. 'About now. Care to go looking for some?'

Her hesitation was only momentary. 'I'd love to,' she said eagerly. 'Should I change my shoes?'

He looked down at her slender feet clad in light sandals. 'Perhaps something a little stouter might be an idea.'

Five minutes later she was back, bare arms and legs covered in insect repellant, low-heeled shoes on her feet. 'Sarah's dead to the world,' she told Justin somewhat breathlessly.

'Once she's off she rarely wakes unless she has a nightmare.'

'Oh. What do you do then?'

'Comfort her. That's all she needs.' He smiled. 'Once she was so distraught that Anna thought it might help if she discussed the dream with her, but she refused, sobbing out that it would frighten Anna, too. Unfortunately I wasn't there.'

Linnet immediately wondered where he had been. On a business trip, no doubt. But perhaps not. Something Bronwyn said floated back, uncomfortably vivid, something about him assuming that Bronwyn had wanted an affair.

As they walked down the paths through the perfumed tangle of the old-fashioned mixture of flower and shrub beds she stole a look at him. Of course he was experienced; it would be very easy for a man possessed of his powers of attraction and that exciting blend of ruthlessness and mastery to interest any woman, except one already in love. It was difficult to imagine that he had lived the life of a celibate since his wife died.

What was strange was her reaction to the idea. It made her feel rather sick.

Hurriedly, before she had time to explore the reasons for this, she said, 'Well, I hope she doesn't have any while we're here.'

'She seems to be growing out of them.'

They had reached a high, strong netting fence, hidden from view by a dense covering of many different creepers. Justin undid the latch of the wooden gate, held it open for Linnet to pass through, then closed it carefully behind them.

And it was another world. The pines continued along the peninsula and beyond the fence to climb the hill which formed the spine of this part of the island, but whereas those on the peninsula swayed above an undergrowth so dense that it would be practically impossible to push through it, here the ground was bare, the roots of the trees forming convoluted patterns across the hillside. The little stream which ran down to the head of the bay was densely embowered in the green arrows of arum lilies, their white flowers eerily vivid in the gathering gloom.

'Incredible!' Linnet breathed. 'Is this all due to wallabies?'

'Not entirely. Cattle and sheep used to run through here, but now that the Maritime Park Board has taken it over as a reserve they've cleared them away. There's some regeneration.'

The ground was slippery with pine needles, it was, no doubt, inevitable that she should trip on the steep path. She was caught before she touched ground, held firmly, then allowed free.

It was just as well she had her back to Justin, or even in that dim light he couldn't have helped seeing the sudden bewildering blush which swept over her in a hot tide.

What's the matter with me? she asked herself.

'You'd better take my hand,' he said calmly. 'It gets steeper.'

'Next time I'll wear boots,' she answered, aware that to refuse his help would be giving the incident exactly that emphasis she wanted to avoid at all costs.

But his hand seemed to scorch her skin and when they reached the top and came out on to a small grassy area she was glad to move away on the pretext of examining a notice-board which asked them to protect and enjoy, and not destroy.

'This is the track down to Mansion House,' he told her. 'If we go across here we might see a wallaby. They quite often come out to graze.'

He walked, panther-quiet, across the grass, made his way between the bushy, fragrant branches of manuka and kanuka, holding them back so that she was not swished by them. After a few seconds he took her hand again, held up a finger in an admonition to silence and slowly, drawing her behind him, made his way to the edge of another grassy clearing, this time completely surrounded by bushes.

And there were the wallabies, two of them, small creatures like a cross between an opossum and a rabbit, one eating while the other kept eyes and ears on the alert. Miraculously they were not disturbed; Linnet held her breath as the feeding one stood up, revealing a tiny head poking from her bulging pouch.

In all her years in Australia she had come no closer to these beautiful, primitive creatures than at the zoo, and now, in New Zealand of all places, she was so close to them that one unwary movement would have sent them scampering off for shelter.

Without the slightest fear they moved across the clearing in the gathering dimness while she stood as still as the man beside her, clutching his hand without realising it.

Then, from below, a dog barked, and they were gone, leaving behind only a reverberating thump, thump, thump, as those strong back legs hit the ground.

'That was marvellous!' Scarcely aware of what she was

doing, she turned to Justin, half laughing with sheer delight. 'Thank you so much for bringing me.'

'My pleasure,' he said coolly, then pulled her close with the hand she had just dropped, while the other splayed across the back of her head, keeping it still.

Linnet met the cold irony of his glance, found that her heart was beating with threatening intensity in her ears. Her whole being screamed out at this violation, but she knew that it would be useless to struggle. Justin would enjoy subduing her, just as he was enjoying her indecision.

'You disappoint me,' she said, trying to infuse the right amount of scorn into her tones.

'Really?' He smiled without humour. 'Because I'm as ready as any other man to accept your invitation? You must think I'm made of ice, Eiluned. You've been pleasantly provocative all evening; I don't like disappointing anyone.'

'I have not been provocative!' She was angry at his calm assumption, furious with herself for behaving in such a manner that he could misunderstand it.

'No?' He smiled again, lowered his head so that his mouth rested on her forehead and spoke quietly against the skin. 'You have, as you damned well know. The restlessness, the lowered voice, the eagerness to come up here with me—the trip on the path. I'd be a fool not to have realised what you want.'

'You're an arrogant, conceited, oversexed fool!' she flung back at him, horrified to find that her voice was trembling. 'You asked for a truce and like a fool I thought you meant it.'

He laughed. 'My dear girl, so I did. This is a very pleasant bonus.'

Gritting her teeth, to hide the fear that his self-control gave her she retorted, 'I am not your dear girl! Will you please let me go? I will not be treated like a—like a flirtatious moron!'

'Why aren't you struggling?'

'Oh!' She stamped her foot in rage, trying to believe

that it was only anger which made her tremble. 'You'd like that, wouldn't you, so that you could prove just how strong you are. Will you let me go? You've spoilt every-thing!'

'In that case—' he murmured, lifting her chin with fingers which allowed no resistance, '—I might as well blot my copybook properly.'

The kiss was devastation, a relentless attack on her mouth and sensibilities, the act of a pirate intent upon his own pleasure and gain, caring not at all who he hurt in the process.

Blood drummed in her ears as she pushed futilely at the hard muscles of his chest. Then, when she thought he wanted to smother her, she folded her fist and hit him just below the ribs. With her foot she caught his shin, and as he straightened up, arched herself away, ready for flight.

But he did not let her go, though she must have hurt him. Instead his lips drew back in a snarl, those eyes blazed with demonic purpose and he laughed deep in his throat. Man the hunter, that icy self-control removed by pain and her resistance; Linnet felt real fear as she rea-lised that she had loosed a demon. This was the man who had driven one woman to suicide. She could believe it now.

'You little bitch!' Justin dragged her against him, both hands pinioned in one of his behind her so that she was unable to resist without further inflaming him by the movement of her body. She stiffened, waiting for another onslaught like the last, her eyes enormous in her face, her bruised mouth held firmly straight. She would *not* show her fear!

For a long moment he stared at her, then the fierce glare died from his eyes, to be replaced by a cold mockery which repelled her even more.

Her breath came in gasps through her lips, but she managed defiance. 'Will you please let me go?' she asked. 'I imagine you've had your kicks.'

'On the contrary.' He released her, put a hand on either side of her face and held it still, surveying her with unsparing intensity. 'You were quite right when you said I would enjoy subduing you to my will. But brute force is too easy—it lacks finesse. I prefer this way . . .'

His mouth touched the sensitive skin at the base of her throat, moved with soft insistence up the vulnerable length to rest in that other hollow beneath one ear. Although she was rigid with outrage Linnet was too relieved at the departure of his anger to resist as she would almost have certainly done otherwise; beside, she found to her horror that some sort of magic was getting through to her, weaving a spell of glamour which threatened her more than the anger of a moment ago.

'*No!*' she exclaimed loudly, using the sound of her voice to bring back sanity.

But he ignored her and his mouth continued to move over her face as if he were blind and he could only see by touch. When his lips closed her eyes she began to tremble, caught by the potent attraction she had subconsciously feared from the moment of meeting him.

'You're frightened,' he whispered, half mocking, half surprised. 'Just relax . . .'

When she tried to answer him he kissed her mouth, softly at first, then with increasing urgency, using his considerable expertise to win some response from her.

But Linnet could only recall that young wife who had been wilful and laughing before she married him, and Bronwyn, who hoped to marry him. And for some strange reason slow tears forced themselves beneath her lashes.

'Eiluned!' Justin sounded startled, his massive self-confidence gone for the moment, and his hands fell from her head.

Impelled by a feeling as primitive as it was overwhelming she took flight, running through the bushes as fleetly as a deer. He called once, then there was silence, except for the soft sound of her feet on the grass and the harshness of her breathing.

Miraculously she arrived at the gate in one piece, having negotiated the track without slipping once. As she raced through it she glanced over her shoulder, but there was no sign of him in the thickening darkness beneath the pines.

By the time she had showered in the small bathroom between her and Sarah's bedrooms it was dark enough to go to bed. Wrapped in her white towelling gown, she paced across her dark room, feeling a desolation of spirit which appalled her by its intensity. It was, she told herself, because she hated the thought of being taken for a cheap flirt and treated with such casual intimacy that it was an insult.

But deeper down she knew that the reason she felt so— so wearily disappointed was because Justin had been revealed as a man who thought he was entitled to take what he wanted even though he was almost engaged to another. Poor Bronwyn—and poor Alison, who must have known that blind fury which had so frightened Linnet.

After a while she sat on her bed, staring through the window at the moon, triumphant as it rose above the hills across the harbour. For once its beauty failed to thrill her, as she wrestled with the realities of the situation she seemed to have got herself into.

Blast Sarah and her tantrum, exacting promises that were going to be so hard to keep! But she could not really blame the child, in spite of the fact that it was she who had got Linnet into this pickle. Blast Justin Doyle, rather! The arrogance of the man repelled her, but when she thought of those moments spent in his power the only thing she could recall was the tide of sensual hunger which had swept over her, blotting out for a few seconds the principles she had always thought so firmly rooted within.

So that was desire. Incredibly, it was the first time she had ever been at its mercy. And, quite frankly, she didn't care if it never happened again. Bronwyn was right: to lose control was a shaming thing to happen, especially as she was prepared to believe that he had felt nothing so earth-shaking. That had been indolent lust in his mouth and voice, not the kind of shattering need she had felt.

No doubt, she thought waspishly, driving the point hard in, if she had shown willing he would have enjoyed himself with some heavy lovemaking, but retained enough control not to seduce her.

And that was humiliation. To be treated as a toy, something to while away a few otherwise boring minutes and then discarded when he went on to the important things of life.

Resolutely she vowed never to be alone with him, never to put herself in such a position again.

Fortified by this resolution, she surprised herself by going to sleep almost instantly.

CHAPTER FIVE

'DADDY came in and kissed me goodbye,' Sarah told her importantly after breakfast the next morning. 'Did he see you, Linnet?'

Linnet drained her orange juice. 'No, he didn't. The seaplane woke me up as it was leaving.'

And just as well, too. The last person she wanted to see was Justin; indeed, the week until she must see him again seemed far too short a time.

It passed quickly too, in weather as warm and settled as early summer could produce. Sarah and Linnet swam and tanned, walked over the hills in search of wallabies, explored the gracious grounds of Mansion House and the restored interior, went fishing with Rob and learned how to cook with Cherry.

Each afternoon Sarah slept for an hour or so while Linnet wrote, and both were astounded at how early they went to bed.

'It's the sea air,' Cherry laughed one evening, when Linnet yawned for the second time and it wasn't yet dark.

'Combined with all that exercise,' Linnet grimaced at her legs. 'I'm sure I've got ten more muscles in each leg than I had before! Sarah is certainly filling out, and she's much more energetic than she was when we came up.'

'It's a good place for a holiday.' Rob lit a pipe, dropping the matches for Goori, who mumbled them between his great jaws.

'It must have been fun on the days when the whole family came up every holidays,' Cherry murmured.

Linnet watched as she set another stitch in her tapestry, a delicate thing of violets for a wallhanging. 'All the family? I didn't realise there was a family, apart from Justin.'

'Oh yes; he has a sister in the United States. She's married to a diplomat at the Embassy in Washington. Apparently Justin's parents and the children, plus an assortment of relations, used to come up. Well, you can tell—the place has bedrooms for ten or so, and the extras used to sleep out all around the terraces.'

'The more the merrier, as far as Cherry's concerned,' Rob said mildly. 'She's longing for Justin to marry and have a family.'

Afterwards Linnet could not imagine what made her ask, but she did. 'Do you ever see anything of Stewart Doyle?'

'Yes, on occasions. He enjoys life here.' Cherry sighed. 'Poor chap! All he's ever wanted to do is farm, but because he's brilliant and weak with it he's always done what others wanted. Justin doesn't understand him, of course, he hasn't any idea of what weakness is.'

'Yet the fact that he puts up with Stewart is a kind of weakness, surely.' Linnet didn't want to talk about Justin, but this uncharacteristic compassion of his intrigued her.

'Well, I don't know about that,' Rob said slowly. 'I reckon Justin feels an obligation towards him. Stewart's side of the family hasn't got the money Justin has. Justin used to subsidise him. Stewart became dependent; I reckon Justin feels guilty about it, feels it's his fault. But I don't know. Stewart's mother was a silly woman. *She* ruined him, if anyone did.'

Cherry laughed. 'The worst thing Rob can call anyone is a silly woman. Stewart's mother died before my time. Rob's lived on Kawau all his life, so he knows them all.'

'The old man was a charmer; it was his wife who was tough. Justin gets his looks and his charm from his father, but his strength from his mother.'

Linnet nodded. 'Sarah looks like him too; she's a sensitive little soul, beneath that superficial arrogance.'

'So's Justin,' Cherry told her crisply. 'Oh, he hides it, but it's there.' Folding up her needlework, she asked, 'Anyone for a drink? I'm making tea.'

And that was the end of that. Linnet was left with the impression that the MacCarthys felt they had been a little indiscreet, because there was no further discussion, not even in the long evenings on the terrace, when the darkness made it easy to reminisce and swap confidences.

Well, she was not going to discuss the Doyles with anyone, not even Bronwyn. She had wondered if she should tell her sister of those moments on the hilltop, but had decided against it. Bronwyn was every bit as worldly as Justin, so she must know what he was like. And if that seemed a remarkably cool-headed approach to a marriage—well, Bronwyn was cool-headed and no doubt Justin had decided never to let his heart rule his head again.

But Linnet couldn't help feeling that Justin would be furious if Bronwyn kissed anyone else as he had kissed her. The old double standard, she thought scornfully, as she tried to push the matter from her mind.

The long days slipped by in a golden haze of sunlight until it was the day before Justin was due to pick them up in the seaplane. Over breakfast Rob announced that he was going across to the mainland to do some shopping; Cherry decided to go too, but when appealed to, Sarah shook her head.

'It's nearly our last day. Let's go exploring, Linnet, and take a picnic.'

So it was decided. They would go over the hills to South Harbour, poke around the old copper mine on the coast, and return in time for dinner.

It was a superb day, clear and hazy with heat, but shortly after lunchtime an ominously dark line of clouds began to build up in the east. After looking at it worriedly several times, Linnet decreed an early return home, and in spite of Sarah's protest insisted on their departure.

It was just as well. Although it was still breathless hot and still when they arrived back there was no doubt that something nasty was building up and would soon be on them.

As they went around closing windows and bringing in outdoor furniture, Linnet couldn't help glancing anxiously at the dark sea between them and the mainland. If Rob had seen the weather coming he and Cherry would be on their way back by now. They had gone in the runabout, and although she knew little about the capabilities of the power boat she was almost certain it wouldn't be able to take too much in the way of wind and sea.

When it seemed that the weather must break, that further tension would be unbearable, the hush was broken by the hum of the seaplane as it landed over the hill at Mansion House.

'Bet he'll head back quickly,' Sarah said quietly, slipping her hand into Linnet's as they waited.

Sure enough, within seconds it seemed, the little plane was gone, fleeing back to Auckland before the storm.

It broke five minutes later with a howl of winds which shipped up waves even in the shelter of the harbour. What it was like further out in the bay Linnet didn't like to think, comforting herself with the reflection that Rob was wise in the ways of this area of the coast. He wouldn't have set off if there had been any danger.

'Gosh, it's got *dark*!' Sarah exclaimed, her voice pitched a little higher than normal.

'Let's play chess, shall we? And you can help me if I make a silly move.'

Sarah loved this, feeling superior for once in her life to an adult. So they settled down in the big living room with the lights on and began their game. It was after three when they began; some time later when the wind and rain showed no signs of abating, Linnet went out to put the kettle on. It had turned cold, and she thought cocoa would be a good idea for Sarah.

A tap on the door made her turn sharply, the cocoa caddy in her hand. Through the glass she could see the figure of a man, streaming with rain.

'Rob!' she exclaimed, running to the door. But it was Justin, the rain darkening his hair to black, streaming down his face and saturating his suit.

'Good heavens!' she exclaimed blankly, then, 'Come in

quickly, I'll get some towels.'

He had started to undress by the time she and Sarah arrived back with armfuls of towels from the hot water cupboard, for his jacket and shirt were deposited in a heap on the porch floor. The sight of his glistening muscular torso gave Linnet an odd sensation in her bones. Ignoring it, she handed the towels to him, then hurried Sarah back into the house.

'Come on, let's get the shower going. He must be freezing.'

His bathroom was warmly walled in pine, with louvre-doored fitments and a tortoiseshell étagère to hold folded towels. It looked masculine and austere and rich, all at once.

'Not in there,' Sarah said bossily. 'That's the sauna. Here's the shower.'

'Turn it on, there's a good girl.'

When she had regulated it to her satisfaction Sarah grabbed another towel and fled, leaving Linnet to look around her, wondering if there was anything else she could do. Her eyes fell on a heater above head height. She switched it on, turned to walk out, suddenly conscious of after-shave and hairbrushes, the paraphernalia of a man's toilet.

Justin met her in the doorway, a towel casually draped around his hips, his features set in an expression of ironic amusement.

'Thank you,' he said gravely, standing aside to let her through.

It was useless to wish she didn't blush so easily. She couldn't think of one sensible thing to say, so she made an indeterminate noise and left as quickly as possible, retaining an image of almost blatant masculinity which so unnerved her that she had to consciously think about making cocoa and heating some tomato soup Cherry had left tucked away in the fridge.

Within ten minutes he was back, dressed in slacks and a knit shirt, only his hair still wet and sleek as sealskin.

Primed by Linnet, Sarah remained comparatively

silent while he drank the soup and ate toast, but when he started on his coffee she could no longer contain herself.

'Where did you come from, Daddy?'

'From the seaplane. It landed at Mansion House with one of the Marine Board chaps on it, and as it was Friday I knew Rob and Cherry would be on the mainland, so I decided to walk across the hills.'

'I could have rowed the dinghy out if he'd brought you round here.' Sarah was inclined to be indignant, but added, 'Anyway, Linnet is very good in it.'

His glance slipped across Linnet's shuttered face, smoothly assessing. 'I wasn't to know that. I thought I could make it before the storm broke, but I didn't.'

'But we didn't expect you till tomorrow,' Sarah pursued. 'Why did you come up today?'

'To see you, of course.'

Her features grew radiant. 'Truly?'

'And to give Linnet this.'

'This' was an envelope, addressed to her and stamped with the Auckland City Council logo.

Linnet felt herself grow pale, and was quite unable to repress the trembling of her fingers as she tore it open.

Her eyes scanned the letter inside, then she gave a whoop of joy, picked Sarah up bodily and kissed her, yelling, 'I've got it, I've got it, I've *got* it!'

Sarah's arms twined themselves around her neck as she almost throttled her with excitement.

'Goody, goody, goody!' she chanted, and then, mischievously, 'You'd better kiss Daddy too, as he brought it up for you.'

Laughingly Linnet dropped the child on to her feet.

'I doubt if he'd expect such a payment for being a postman,' she said, wishing that Sarah had chosen some other time and person to exercise her sense of humour on.

'I can think of nothing more pleasant,' he grinned, coolly leaning back in his chair to survey her with a glance which openly dared her.

Linnet hesitated, than an imp of devilry drove her to bend, drop a kiss on his cheek and retreat, aware that she had allowed him to provoke her into a false position.

'Coward!' he taunted gently.

Sarah became belligerent. 'I think it was a very nice kiss.'

'Just the right sort of kiss for a little girl to give,' he agreed blandly, a derisive note clear in his voice. Without changing expression, he asked, 'When do you start?'

'After the New Year.'

'Not very far away.'

Sarah clamoured to know how far Christmas was away, and when her father told her danced in her turn, chanting a hymn to Christmas, asking afterwards, 'What do you want, Linnet?'

'Oh—nothing, really. I've everything I need.'

'But Christmas is a time for things to want, and things to give, not for things to *need*!'

She laughed at the disgust in the childish tones. Then I'd like a happy year. Can you give me that?'

Justin said, 'You can give her that.'

'Happiness comes from within,' she snapped, angry with him for forcing the issue into the open. Had he no care for the child at all? If Sarah knew that Linnet had refused to become her companion she would view her refusal as yet another rejection, and heaven knew she had had enough of those in her short life.

Father and daughter regarded her. It was strange that two identical pairs of eyes could be so different. Sarah's were thoughtful, a little surprised at the tone of her adored companion's voice, but there was a kind of unholy mockery darkening the paleness of her father's glance which was as challenging as it was maddening.

Linnet found herself hoping that the child's clear vision would never be marred by such an expression, and for the first time realised that for Justin there must have been rejections too, of a nature she could not possibly comprehend, for once he, too, must have possessed the innocence of his daughter.

Through all of the other emotions he stirred in her, the potent attraction to her senses, the unwilling respect and pleasure in his intelligence, the dislike of his ruthlessness, the fear of his cruelty, a new one struggled to life—compassion. Perhaps only God knew what had happened over the years to him, but cynicism was always hardly bought, so the road to his present state of mind had not been an easy one. For him, or for the others who had combined to make of him the man he was, she thought sombrely, and that she had better not forget.

'You look funny,' said Sarah, uncertainty making her hesitate before the last word.

Like her father, she saw too much. 'Do I? Perhaps it's the storm. Justin, what's likely to happen?'

'Just this. A downpour, thunder and lightning, but by tomorrow morning the winds will have died away and it might be fine again.'

A gleam of something—amusement?—had flared in his eyes for a moment, but as he spoke he rose and walked across to the window to stand with his back to them. After a moment he continued, 'The power is almost certain to go off. I'll check the generator.'

'Will you get wet again?'

As soon as she had said the words Linnet could have bitten her tongue out. For all the world like a fussy, not too bright wife!

That fugitive gleam showed once more as he turned to face her. 'No, Eiluned, I won't get wet. I'll use Rob's oilskins, and the generator room is not far away anyway.'

Sarah said, 'Why don't you call her Linnet, like I do? It's easier to say, and she told me that it's a proper contraction.' She produced the last word triumphantly, like a conjuror with a rabbit.

'She might not like it,' he replied gravely, though the glance which came Linnet's way was sharply satirical.

'Would you mind?' Sarah asked.

Thus appealed to, Linnet shrugged, strangely on the defensive. 'No, why should I? It's easier to say.'

'There you are, Daddy. You can call her Linnet.'

'Do you mind?'

The question should have been casual, merely a well-bred gesture, but the softness of his voice and the hooded, strangely aloof expression gave it some hidden meaning which Linnet could not discern.

Assailed by an odd breathlessness, she said stiffly, 'Not in the least. I know some people object to having their names shortened, but Mother always calls me Linnet, so I've grown used to it.'

'Ah, yes, your mother. Do you hear from her much?'

Sheer surprise and antagonism with it brought a sparkle of colour to her cheeks; he had no right to use that slighting tone of voice to refer to her mother.

'Every week,' she said briskly, beginning to clear away the dishes from the small table in the kitchen as a signal that she wasn't interested in continuing any conversation on that topic.

Justin seemed oblivious of her intention. 'A devoted mother indeed,' he replied with a dry hard emphasis which brought a glitter to the golden depths of her eyes.

But she was determined not to show her anger, especially not in front of Sarah. So she said merely, 'Very,' and with compressed lips went about washing the dishes. Sarah dried and put away, and Justin poured himself another cup of coffee and drank it, and although she refused to look in his direction she knew he was watching her.

It was a relief when he finally left them to check the generator, but only a temporary one, for she realised that as his arrival was unexpected it was unlikely that Cherry had done anything like making his bed up. And for some strange reason her whole being rose up in rebellion at the thought of doing it herself.

But it would have to be done, so she said brightly to Sarah, 'Let's go and see if Dad's bed is ready for him, shall we?'

'O.K. I know where the sheets are kept—in the hall cupboard outside his door.'

The room was larger than her own small one, and again there was that clever mixture of starkness of line combined with extreme luxury of fittings. As she checked beneath the velvet of the bitter chocolate bedspread she admitted that probably this did represent the true nature of the man; a hard, straight framework of character with a complex richness of interests which were an extension of his keen brain. And through it all the power that his sensual attraction gave him.

Perhaps the fact that the room was dominated by the bed, an enormous king-sized affair, made her wonder whether he always slept in it alone. The thought stung. With a ruthlessness more typical of him than her she pushed it into the recesses of her mind, setting herself to making the thing with Sarah's willing but unskilful help.

When it was done the child smoothed the nap of the velvet and said proudly, 'That's the first time I've ever made a bed.'

Linnet was startled. 'Not even your own?'

'No. Mrs Le Sueur—Anna—says it's easier for her to do it.'

The age-old cry of the harassed mother. Well, no doubt Anna did have more than enough to keep her busy, even though everything in that house was as labour-saving as modern science could make it, but surely she could find the time to instruct Sarah in the basics of caring for herself. Everyone, male or female, should be able to keep house, Linnet felt, and the sooner they learned the easier it would be.

'Does Cherry make your bed up here?' she asked.

'Yes.'

'Well, how about if we suggest you do it? It would make things easier for her, and you'd learn in no time.'

Sarah grinned. 'Then I'd surprise Mrs Le Sueur. Yes, let's do that.'

'Do what?'

At the sound of her father's voice from the door Sarah ran towards him, her voice eager as she explained.

Above the fair head his eyes met Linnet's. 'That's a good idea. Thank you both for making my bed.'

A subtle note of amusement in his voice made her look away, angered. No doubt he thought that any woman

would be glad to wait on him, she thought, not too co-
herently, and wished she had left the bed strictly alone.
She hoped he would have nightmares in it!

Determined not to be intimidated, she returned lightly,
'Think nothing of it. Nobody likes sleeping between blan-
kets.'

He laughed at that. 'Goodness, you do think I'm a
poor sort, don't you? For your information, Linnet, I've
made my bed more often than you, I'd imagine.'

'Well, seeing I've only made it once——!'

'You know well enough what I mean.'

He was still smiling, that attraction more vivid and
potent than ever in the dim intimacy of his bedroom.

Only by thinking firmly and with great strength of will
of the other women he had no doubt dazzled in this very
room by his superb sexual magnetism was she able to
remain unmoved by it. After swallowing once she answered, 'Yes, I know what you mean. Come on, Sarah,
we'll have to go and work out what to have for dinner. I
doubt if Cherry will be back.'

'Not a hope.' Justin stood aside to let her through the
door just as the telephone shrilled.

'Ah, that will be her now.'

Feeling as if she had escaped from some kind of trap
Linnet wasted no time in making for the instrument.

It was Cherry, very upset, but vastly relieved to hear
that Justin was there.

'Oh, then you'll be all right,' the tiny voice said
happily, far, far away at the end of the line. 'And Rob
can stop worrying about the generator and things.'

'Yes, Justin's already been out to it,' Linnet agreed,
wondering hollowly why Cherry's relief wasn't matched
by her own. 'Listen, what's for dinner?'

'Scotch fillet in the fridge. Just grill it. And I've made
the sauce, it's in the covered gravy boat. Heat it up but
don't let it boil. Any vegetables, Justin's not fussy, but he
likes things cooked properly, so don't boil them to mush.
Give him cheese and fruit for afters.' Cherry's voice
became anxious. 'Can you do some sort of hors d'oeuvres

to start with?'

'Yes, of course I can. Don't worry, Cherry, everything's under control.'

Which was rather a lie, she thought as she relinquished the receiver to Justin, who wanted to speak to Rob. For she had the oddest feeling that she wasn't under control at all. And the thought of staying the night in the house alone with Justin was beginning to assume alarming importance to her.

So she conjured up the image of Bronwyn, who had been so hurt in all her loves that she had retreated behind a mask of cynicism which was as much part of her now as a skin. Bitter indeed to be rejected, first by her father, then by that man she had loved and lost, whoever he had been. It would be too much to discover that the man she wanted to marry thought nothing of making love to her sister. But even though Linnet could think of nothing worse than a marriage held together only by passion and self-interest, it was what Bronwyn wanted. Perhaps she thought such a relationship offered no possibilities of further pain.

Linnet sent a fleeting glance towards Justin as he spoke into the receiver. In the half-light he loomed, one shoulder against the wall, the other hunched slightly as he strained to hear against the rising note of the wind outside, the tense attitude emphasising his magnificent body, handsome face turned away so that all she could see was the predatory line of his profile.

Oh, Bronwyn! she thought wearily. Put yourself in this man's power and the possibilities for pain are practically limitless. As Alison had apparently discovered.

'That's that, then,' he said as he put the receiver back.

The commonplace remark made her smile. 'Yes, that's that.'

'Mocking me, Linnet?'

The soft tone of his voice sent a twinge of excitement across her nerves, but her voice was steady as she replied lightly, 'Nothing so brave. I was agreeing, that's all.'

The glance which flicked across her features was ironic,

but he merely said, 'Rob and Cherry won't get back tonight, and if this wind keeps up they'll have difficulty bringing the runabout across until the sea goes down. Which could be some time tomorrow afternoon.'

'Where will they stay?'

'With Rob's sister in Warkworth.'

A flash of lightning lit up the windows, followed after some seconds by a roll of thunder. Sarah wriggled uneasily, but said nothing, her tight lips hiding what Linnet guessed to be a very real fear of thunder.

'Well, we'd better see about dinner,' she said briskly. 'What's your favourite dessert, Sarah?'

'Jelly and peaches.'

Glancing at her watch, Linnet said, 'We should have time to get the jelly to set before dinner. Let's go.'

Making the jelly took only a few minutes, but Linnet spun out the occasion. Talking to the child helped keep her mind off the man. But afterwards they went into the sitting room to find that he had lit a fire in the stone fireplace and turned off all but one lamp so that the unseasonal darkness outside was matched by the soft light within. Very intimate.

'Just like a family,' as Sarah put it delightedly, pulling Linnet down on to the sofa so that she sat between them. 'Father on one side and mother the other and me in the middle.'

Linnet kept her head low. She did not want to see the satire in Justin's expression at her daughter's innocent remark, for, oddly enough, it would hurt.

'A very young mother,' he commented, his voice smooth 'How old are you, Linnet?'

'Twenty.'

'You were twelve when you left Auckland?'

'Yes.'

Sarah snuggled against her. 'Why did you go, Linnet?'

'My mother and father decided not to live together any more. My mum is from Australia, so she went back home and took me with her.'

'And you never came back until now?'

It was an inquisition, but one that she could not prevent, for the child was looking at her with, the absorbed,
curious expression which she knew meant she was not
going to be satisfied by evasions. And Justin, who could
have stopped his daughter, said nothing.

'No, never.'

'So you didn't see your father at all?' The clear voice
was horrified.

'No.'

'Perhaps you wrote to him?'

Linnet's teeth covered her bottom lip, but she made no
attempt to lie. 'No.' Better to give a bold answer than to
tell the child that after her first three letters had been
returned to her, unopened, she had given up trying to
communicate with her father.

Resentment flamed into life within her. Justin had no
right to allow his daughter to probe like this.

Then he said softly, 'Yet you felt he owed you something.'

And she understood. That wretched inheritance she
was supposed to be claiming! No wonder his main feeling
towards her was one of contempt.

Indeed, looked at from his point of view, she was a
pretty poor specimen of humanity, greedy enough to
want to deprive Bronwyn of half of her heritage yet with
the crashing gall to park herself on her sister when it
suited her.

She hadn't worried overmuch about Bronwyn's use of
her in her schemes before, but for some strong reason she
felt an imperative desire to clear herself in Justin's eyes.
Then she looked across, her eyes wide and imploring in
the soft fireglow, and saw his expression and the impulse
died as swiftly as it had arisen.

The hot blood flooded her cheeks and throat as she
turned her face away, careless that her embarrassment
probably only reinforced Bronwyn's lie. He was a beast,
she thought stormily, a beast of prey who enjoyed the
hunt and the kill. He had set her up very nicely for that
one, but there was no excuse for him to look at her as

though she was a cheap money-grubbing little tramp, whatever he thought of her.

But Justin kept to conventional rules of politeness, even though he broke them in the spirit. And she felt too tired for her usual reaction, spitting at him like an angry kitten with just as much effect, to retort as scathingly as she would like to. Not in front of the child.

So she muttered, 'That's not really anyone's business but mine.'

'And Bronwyn's.'

'And hers,' she agreed, pushing her hair back from suddenly damp temples.

Sensitively attuned to her surroundings, yet unable to understand what was happening between her companions, Sarah broke in peaceably, 'Do you think it will rain tomorrow, Daddy? If it does, will we be able to stay here for another day?'

'If it rains, yes. Unless Linnet wants to get back immediately.'

The note of sarcasm was not lost on Linnet, but she ignored it. 'It makes no odds to me,' she said disdainfully.

'Of course it doesn't!' Sarah turned to her father, enthusiastic and perhaps a little protective. 'Linnet loves it here. She can swim like a fish, Daddy, and she's shown me how to life-save a bit. And she can make a blade of grass scream like a banshee.'

'Can she, indeed? A very worthwhile skill. I used to be able to do it myself.'

'Really and truly?' His daughter eyed him with respect and some wonder. 'Gosh, and you've never shown me how to! Can you do anything else? Linnet can stick her fingers in her mouth and whistle like a shepherd.'

He laughed at this, pulled a tendril of the fine soft hair. 'All of Linnet's tricks seem to be distinctly noisy. Has she got any quiet ones?'

'Telling stories—but you know that. And she can bend her thumbs back on to her wrists. Show Daddy, Linnet.'

The last thing she wanted to do was display her one physical trick to the mocking glance of the man beside her, but it would be churlish to refuse Sarah's proud command. So, obediently, she bent her thumbs back until they touched the narrow length of her wrists.

'Very flexible,' Justin told her, and took her hand in his, moving his thumb over the slender length of hers and the soft width of her palm.

His touch seemed to scorch; she couldn't prevent the automatic jerk backward, but his reaction was totally unexpected. His fingers clamped down on to hers, cruelly holding them in thrall, but his head remained bent as though he found her hands unexpectedly fascinating.

Almost she cried out, but her self-control did not snap. And after a moment he lifted his head, looking her full in the face, his expression bleak and shuttered, the features cold and hard as the ice statue he had been when they first met.

Then he released her, and Sarah said something, and that moment of—*despair?*—was gone.

But after dinner when he was reading to Sarah in her bedroom Linnet sat slumped in a deep, comfortable armchair and wondered. Despair seemed an incongruous state of mind to link with Justin, so strong, so assured and arrogantly certain of his path in life, but she had felt a wave of something very close to it emanating from him at that moment.

Justin despairing? Her mind rejected it. And yet why not? She did not know him very well, in spite of the fact that Bronwyn intended to marry him. Their relationship was a peculiarly public one; he collected Bronwyn from the flat two or three evenings each week and took her to dinner or to the theatre or whatever, delivering her back at the appropriate time. Presumably they made love, but although Linnet had always been in bed when they arrived back, he never stayed long in the flat. And there was no possibility of them using the back seat of his car. So perhaps they called in at the main house before they arrived at the flat.

A pain in her lip brought her the realisation that she was biting it. Stupid—*stupid*—to feel this hollow kind of rage at the vision of her sister in Justin's arms. Only an idiot would allow him to become so important to her.

Her mind picked over the word, hesitating, rejecting. Important. Was that what he had become? Could he be important, not as Sarah's father, not as Bronwyn's man, but as Justin Doyle?

Two fingers pushed the frown away from between her brows, an old habit she still had when worried. As they smoothed the skin of her forehead, up and down, up and down, some of the tension engendered by the questions she asked herself eased away, but she knew the relaxation was only temporary.

For the first time in her life she found herself trying to evade an issue. So important a subject must be thought through in peace and quiet, she told herself, springing to her feet just as Justin came back into the room.

'You look poised for flight,' he commented.

Immediately she felt foolish. 'I was going to look out of the window,' she answered, her voice defensive.

'Go ahead, although you won't be able to see much.'

He was right, of course. A glance at her watch revealed that the sun had probably just set, but the heavy clouds and the rain had made it dark much earlier than usual.

All she could see through the wet panes was the reflection of the room behind her. And Justin Doyle, motionless in the doorway, so still that he reminded her of her fantasy of him as a beast of prey.

A bubble of tension filled her throat. Nervously she put out a hand to draw the curtains across; the storm outside forced the realisation of her isolation upon her, but after a moment she turned away without touching the draperies. It would be even more intimate to be cocooned within their warmth with him, hidden from the blackness outside.

'Are you nervous?'

She shrugged, keeping her head turned away.

'Not really; we do have storms in Australia, you know.'

Perhaps he caught the barely repressed note of tension in her tones, for he nodded, saying without emphasis,

'Yes, I know Infinitely more dramatic than anything
over here. I've been through a hurricane there.'

It seemed a safe enough subject. 'Where?' she asked.

'At Darwin.'

This did surprise her. 'The big one?'

'Yes.' He had sat down in the modern leather chair
which should have been a stark intruder in the comfortable room, but somehow blended perfectly. 'Sit down,
Linnet. I'm not going to eat you.'

A faint flush touched her cheeks at this recognition of
her fears, but she obeyed, choosing a chair on the very
edge of the pool of light cast by the single lamp. In the
semi-darkness he was still, the arrogant lines of his features clear cut against the darkness of the leather. He
wore a black shirt and black trousers; on most men it
would have been an overly dramatic colour scheme, but
he had enough bravura to carry it off.

He pleases the eye, she thought suddenly, feeling her
flush deepen as somewhere in the pit of her stomach
something twisted, a sensation not entirely pleasurable.

Hastily, in a voice artificially brisk, she asked, 'What
was it like?'

'The hurricane?' At her nod he resumed drily, 'Unpleasant. I was staying with friends. We spent the night
in their bathroom which was built of concrete and there-
fore the strongest room in the house. Rosalie had just
come home with a new baby. It was a long night.'

Linnet nodded again. 'I can imagine. What happened
next day?'

'Oddly enough, I quite enjoyed that. We came
through unscathed, although the house was a shambles.
After we'd settled Rosalie and the child we found our-
selves in the thick of reorganisation.' He smiled. 'If you'd
been there then your opinion of me would have been
reinforced. I had to be aggressive, rude, ruthless—all the
things you've called me.'

'I haven't!' She was appalled, and bewildered. This
was a new Justin, subtly teasing, without that chilling
mask she had always sensed before.

'Perhaps not,' he said almost indulgently, pale eyes tantalising, 'but you've thought them all. Admit it.'

'Not without reason,' she protested, unsure of herself as she had never been before.

'I'll grant you that.'

There didn't seem to be any sort of reply to that. After a moment she asked, 'Would you like some coffee?'

He laughed, 'Yes, thank you.'

At last she escaped from the room, but as she set the tray she found her heart was beating erratically and there wasn't anything she could do about it. Telling herself not to be stupid made no difference, nor did her fierce injunctions to think of Bronwyn. Bronwyn seemed someone known in another world, as distant in time and space as the outermost stars of the galaxy. The only reality was this house, warm and hidden by the encircling storm, and the man who sat in the chair in the living room.

When she returned he set aside his book and accepted the cup from her with a smile which was both mocking and indulgent. They talked for a time about Sarah, Linnet forgetting her selfconsciousness as she told him of his daughter's behaviour, revealing her own growing affection for the child in every word, every expression which touched her sensitive features.

'She certainly seems fitter,' he commented. 'Can I not persuade you to give up the idea of becoming a librarian and be Sarah's companion?'

'No.' She shook her head firmly. 'And it's not playing fair to try emotional blackmail, Justin. Sarah doesn't really need a companion.'

'No. She needs a mother.'

From beneath her lashes she darted a swift glance across the pool of light. Her heart contracted with compassion as she saw he looked tired as he stared into his coffee cup, the long, strong fingers clenched around the handle.

Then he looked up and smiled with irony. 'Don't look so upset, Linnet. Why should you worry about Sarah? Until a few weeks ago you didn't even know she existed.'

She felt as though he had taken her feelings and slapped her with them, the rebuff was so plain. All of her old antagonism came flooding back.

'True. But I know now, and thanks to you, I've seen enough of her to become concerned.'

'Oh, lord, I'm not blaming you. After all, the maternal instinct is supposed to be strong in most women, isn't it?'

There was something so savagely sarcastic in his voice that she pressed herself back against the firm back of her chair, aware that somehow the conversation had managed to stray into a minefield.

'Isn't it?' he asked again, setting the cup and saucer down on the low table beside him.

Striving desperately for lightness, a way to ease the tension, she answered, 'How should I know? Between psychologists and radicals, we women don't know what we are. Ask me in forty years' time. I might be able to give you the benefit of my experience. Until then, I won't answer.'

'On the grounds that you might incriminate yourself?' His smile was without humour, a flash of white in the darker shadow of his face. 'You're an enigma, Linnet. You look like Botticelli's redheaded dream of sensuous spring, yet you treat your sister with a hard practicality more like a modern businessman. You're obviously fond of Sarah, but you won't put yourself out for her at all.'

'Put myself out!' The words almost sputtered from her lips, so angry was she. 'What you want me to do is give up my future for her. I won't——'

'Don't shout,' he interposed smoothly, coldly. 'If you fell in love and decided to marry, would you still keep on with this decision?'

'Of course I would. Marriage doesn't——' For the second time she was interrupted, but this time by the ominous flickering of the light before it went out with a finality which made her gasp and jump to her feet.

CHAPTER SIX

JUST like the entrance of the Demon King, she thought, as lightning lashed, followed by an enormous roll of thunder which echoed around the sky. Across the room she heard Justin swear, then he said crisply, 'The power is off. Wait where you are and I'll switch the generator on.'

Outside all hell seemed to be breaking loose. In the intermittent flare of lightning Linnet saw that he was gone. After what seemed far longer than necessary a light flicked on in the kitchen. Only one, however, and when she tried a switch in the living room nothing happened.

'It's AC, not DC,' said Justin as he came in through the door. 'There's one switch in each room wired to DC. The generator is really a relic of the days when the power supply to the island was very erratic, but it comes in useful on occasions such as this, so we keep it in working order.'

'Do Cherry and Rob live here during the winter?'

He nodded. 'Rob is a potter, as I suppose you know. He's very good, but still getting established. Perhaps one day he'll want to go, but I hope not. The place won't be the same without them.'

'Has he always lived here?'

'His parents tried to farm here, but it was too hard, and when my father built this place they moved into the cottage. I can remember when Rob was born. His parents were almost middle-aged, and they were thrilled. I was five or six, and he was the first baby I'd ever had anything to do with,' he smiled somewhat sardonically. 'My memories of him are mainly of a kid with a mop of curls, trailing me around, determined to do everything I did.'

'He must have been a nuisance.' Just why she said that

Linnet couldn't fathom, except that she simply couldn't imagine Justin acting nursemaid for a child.

'Oh, he was,' he returned coolly. 'But I admired his determination.'

Which meant that he must have accepted the responsibility; probably the reason for the easy friendship between the two men now. Linnet leaned back in her chair, trying to visualise the Justin Rob had followed. He would have been a handsome boy; had he always worn that mask of chilling reserve, or could that be laid at the door of his experience with Alison? Somehow it had become important to know what Alison was like. Stewart had said that she was stupid, but that had not stopped him from loving her or Justin from marrying her. And the child she had made with him was certainly not stupid. Apart from that she knew only that they resembled each other slightly. Sarah's treasured photograph showed a young girl, not like Linnet in feature at all, but Stewart had said that the colouring was similar.

'What are you thinking of?'

She looked startled by the thread of anger in his voice. Of course he couldn't read her thoughts! But he certainly looked as though he could; there was a darkening of his features that warned of emotions held on a tight rein.

'Just thinking,' she retorted, deliberately vague. And swiftly, 'Justin, what does Stewart do for you?'

His expression hardened into hauteur. 'He works for the organisation. Why?'

It was obviously foolish to carry on, but she had developed an affection for Stewart over the past few weeks. Exasperating though he was, his wry acceptance of his faults, his lack of the usual pretences which weak people often hide behind to conceal their weaknesses from themselves endeared him to her. And she knew he was unhappy.

'I just wondered,' she said lamely.

He leaned forward, that tough expression once more predominant. 'Don't let him play on your sympathy,' he advised hardly. 'He's an expert at it, and it means nothing. He's had more chances than most and taken none of them.'

'So Bronwyn said.'

He took her up on this swiftly. 'Bronwyn?'

'Yes.' Linnet was uncertain now what to say. If he was going to be annoyed by Bronwyn's discussion of his cousin's weaknesses she certainly wasn't going to say anything about it.

But he merely said, 'Bronwyn dislikes waste of any sort, so she finds Stewart very irritating. He goes out of his way to antagonise her, of course. It's his usual method of making himself unpopular. Do you see much of him?' The question was abrupt, flung at her with a hard swiftness which made her blink.

'Well—not much. He comes down sometimes in the evening, but he never stays for long.'

'Just don't let your sympathetic heart see another Sarah in him,' he told her with a narrow smile. 'Stewart is quite happy, but he isn't averse to playing on the sympathies of an attractive woman. He's tried it with Bronwyn, but she's experienced enough to see him for what he is.'

'And what is he?'

The broad shoulders moved in the slightest of shrugs. Irrelevantly Linnet remembered the hard warmth of them against her hands the evening he had kissed her. Swift colour surged into her cheeks as she lowered her head, thanking the storm for the dimness of the light.

'Stewart suffers from the ingrained belief that the world owes him—everything,' he told her harshly. 'That's all, but it's been like a poisonous blight over his life. When you have children, Linnet, be very careful what you tell them. There's nothing so powerful as a mother's frustrated desires projected on to her children. Unless it's guilt at one's undeserved good fortune.'

So Rob had been right, and Justin blamed first his aunt and then himself for the lack of willpower in Stewart's character. And because he was Justin, who was not one to shirk a responsibility, he kept Stewart by his side, probably not realising that he was increasing his cousin's habit of dependence. Or perhaps he just didn't care.

Linnet couldn't help wondering whether what she thought of his mask, that icy strength which so well hid his emotions, was, in reality, the whole man, and the only emotions he allowed himself were the impersonal ones of responsibility, courage—and desire. Perhaps being unable to love, he deliberately chose for his wife Bronwyn, who did not want to love again.

Then she remembered Sarah, and knew that she was only partly right. His love of his daughter was obvious in a hundred small ways, even to the extent of forcing him to permit a person he despised into his house. Which person being Eiluned Grant, who found herself in the far from enviable state of being physically drawn to him as much as she was emotionally afraid of him.

What a situation! A bleak smile touched her lips as she wondered whether something in her make-up ensured that she should become involved with those men who married her closest relations. First David—now almost a ghost—and then Justin, who was dangerous as David had never been.

And from whom it would be infinitely more difficult to run, for she had promised Sarah to stay.

'You seem amused,' he interrupted her thoughts with cold irritation, standing as he spoke.

The lamplight caught his hair, turning the ends and the highlights to a tawny shade beneath which the grey eyes lost what colour they possessed. Viking-tall, he moved with silent gait across to the window, drawn, perhaps, by the same instincts which had taken Linnet there earlier in the evening, a primitive pleasure at being out of the storm, warm and dry and secure.

Against their conversation the wind had been increasing in intensity, pouncing on the house with the wilful cruelty of a cat playing with its prey, so that the windows rattled in the fiercer gusts, adding their noise to that of the storm.

'It seems to be getting worse,' she said on an indrawn

breath. 'I hope nobody got caught in it.'

Justin looked through the windows with sombre intensity.

'God help them if they are, because there's nothing anybody can do for them. Are you frightened?'

'No,' she denied, too quickly to be convincing.

'It won't last long at this rate. Before morning it will have blown itself out. Why don't you go to bed and get some sleep?'

'I don't think I could sleep with this racket going on.'

He moved away from the windows, a slight smile softening his expression. 'The house is built strongly enough to take any storm, even if the windows do rattle slightly. Choose a record to put on and I'll give you a game of chess.'

'Chess?' She couldn't prevent the dismay which coloured her voice. 'Couldn't we play something a little simpler—like Snakes and Ladders?'

He laughed at that but shook his head. 'That's pure chance. How about Chinese Checkers?'

'Well—all right, but there's altogether too much thinking to be done in that for my liking,' she retorted, aware that she should have taken his suggestion and retired for the night. If she had any sense at all she would be snugly tucked up in her bed, away from his disturbing personality and the danger he represented.

Perhaps she was a fool, but she declined to compound her foolishness by putting on the sort of record which seemed to predominate. Music to make love by, she thought grimly, finally selecting a disc of light classics. Pleasant and innocuous, with no erotic undertones to emphasise the fact that she was almost alone in the house with the most enigmatic, interesting man she had ever met.

As it was, she found the experience of playing a child's game with him extremely unsettling. The setting was almost too dramatic to be credible, the shrieking wind outside, the comfortable room with its circle of lamplight enclosing them in intimate softness, the man, handsome

as a Nordic god, intent on beating her at the simple
game. And when he had won, and the record had
finished, he changed it for one of Cleo Laine singing love
songs, the brilliant voice sensuous in the stagey atmosphere.

'Do you play backgammon?' he asked lazily, settling
himself on to the sofa beside her.

'No. And I don't think I want to learn,' she returned,
stiffening slightly at his proximity.

'Why do you pretend to be stupid? I know you're intelligent.'

'I just haven't got the right brain for games.' She
wanted to move away, but felt herself caught in the brilliance of his glance, ensnared like a moth by a candle.

Justin was smiling as though he knew that fire licked
along her veins, lifting her to a totally new plane of existence. With eyes which were wide pools of pure gold about
a black centre Linnet stared down at her hands, aware
that they were trembling very slightly. The singer's voice
floated over them, lazy yet filled with longing, surprisingly strong against the elemental background of the
storm without, barely able to make itself heard over the
storm which raged within Linnet's breast.

With a kind of fatalistic courage she knew that she
wanted him, wanted to lose herself in the strength of his
arms and body, ease the torment of her need by surrend-
ing to it. It would be easily accomplished, she was not
particularly experienced, but she sensed that he desired
her as much as she wanted him.

If only he would make the first move. . . .

Abruptly she looked up, met the fierce demand of his
eyes, and found her breath coming heavily through her
lips. But he did not move a muscle, though she could feel
the intense self-control he was exerting. So he would not
seduce her against her will. If she spent the rest of the
night in his bed it would be at her desire, not because he
had overborne her protests with the glamour of his practised lovemaking. No, he was relying on the strong sexual
attraction which sparked between them to persuade her

into his arms.

And she knew she could not.

'I think I'd better get to sleep,' she said on an indrawn breath, the words coming raggedly through her lips as she fought his dangerous attraction with every scrap of will power.

'Very well.' He showed no anger, not even disappointment. 'I'll show you which light goes on.'

'No—you don't need to.' The idea of him in her bedroom was unbearable.

He smiled, a cold movement of his mouth. 'Very well. It's the switch by the window.'

Once in her room she put the light on, pulled the curtains across the window and without thought went into the bathroom she shared with Sarah, where she washed her face with cold water. The trembling she had noticed in her hands had by now spread to her whole body, she felt as though she had a high fever which the cold water did nothing to abate.

But when she was at last in the warmth of her bed, surrounded by the friendly darkness, she found she was crying, softly yet hopelessly, as if she had been betrayed. And long hours later, when the wind had died and there was only the sound of the rain thrumming on the iron roof, she found it in herself to be grateful that Justin had not tried to persuade her, and thankful that she had possessed enough of the instinct for self-preservation to leave him alone in the living room.

By the time she woke the next morning even the rain had stopped, and the sun was out in a sky so blue that it hurt her eyes.

'The sea is still up,' Sarah told her, 'but the power's back on, and Daddy says it won't be long before Mr and Mrs McCarthy are back.'

Linnet found it was possible to smile in spite of the fact that she seemed to have a stone in the middle of her chest. Sarah had brought her in a cup of coffee—instant—and a rosebud, not scathed at all by the storm. Earnest and rather proud of her expertise, Sarah was very endearing, and when Linnet dropped a kiss on the top of her head she looked up with her heart in her eyes.

'That was nice,' she exclaimed breathlessly. 'Linnet, I *do* like you! You look like a flower, a flower on a long stem, all graceful and slender.'

Touched by the patent sincerity in her eyes and voice, Linnet gave her a swift hug. 'That's the nicest compliment anyone has ever paid me, heart's delight. Have you given your father his coffee?'

'Oh, he's been up for ages. He went for a swim almost before the sun was up, I think.'

As Linnet sipped her coffee she worried about meeting Justin again after last night. But when she had dressed and made her way into the kitchen she realised she had worried unnecessarily.

He sent her a swift, cool assessment of a glance, then nodded. 'Good morning, Linnet.'

Shamefully, she was somewhat piqued by his lack of emotion.

'Good morning, Justin.'

'Can I cook you a flounder? I found three in the fridge.'

'Can you?'

He smiled ironically at that, but replied mildly enough, 'I can't claim Cordon Bleu status, but I can produce a reasonable meal, given time.'

The fish were delicious, simply fried and served with slices of lemon and tufts of parsley which Sarah insisted on scattering over them.

'Just the right sizes,' she announced with satisfaction, 'A father-sized one, a mother-sized one for you, Linnet, and a littler one for me. We're a family!'

There were times, Linnet decided, when the innocence of youth was downright embarrassing. Head lowered, she didn't dare to look at the man opposite her.

In an amused voice he responded, 'True, but Linnet is too young to be your mother, honey.'

'Not too young to be your wife, though,' his daughter countered swiftly. 'She's not too young for that, is she?'

There was a moment of silence, then Justin's urbane tones, 'She might think so. Eleven years is quite a difference in ages, when one is as young as Linnet. What *do* you think, Linnet?'

Fortunately she had a mouthful, so she was granted a few moments' respite while she chewed what had suddenly turned into flannel. Then in a voice which sounded a little like her own she answered, 'It depends entirely on the people concerned, surely.'

'Ah, but given the people concerned,' Justin goaded smoothly, 'what do you think? Am I too old for you?'

It took all her self-control not to fling her plate and its contents at him, but one glance at Sarah's upturned, interested face prevented her from answering as waspishly as she would have liked.

Calling to her aid her most non-committal tones, she returned, 'I can't really say, never having viewed you in that light. But there have been happy marriages with a greater difference in age than that.' And driven by the desire to hurt him, she added, 'And unhappy ones with little or no difference in age at all.'

Her courage failed completely when it came to looking at him. But from the steel in his tones when he spoke she knew her shaft had gone home.

'Very true, Linnet.'

The rest of the meal tasted like ashes in her mouth.

After breakfast she tidied up the house, determined that Cherry shouldn't return to more work than was necessary. Sarah wanted to help, but when her father appeared at the door suggesting a walk along the beach to see what the storm had brought up, she couldn't help directing a pleading glance at her companion.

'Off you go,' Linnet told her, half laughing. 'If you find anything exciting bring it back, won't you?'

'You come too,' Sarah suggested.

Picking up the hose of the vacuum cleaner, Linnet shook her head. 'No, love, I'm going to finish this. You head off, now.'

'Daddy, tell Linnet she can come with us!'

Without expression he said, 'Let her be, Sarah. I can't tell her what to do.'

When they had gone Linnet found that her temples were wet with perspiration and the hand that pushed the cleaner hose across the floor was shaking. If only she could go back in time to breakfast and unsay that last below-the-belt jibe! Even though Justin had taunted her it had been unforgivable to retaliate so maliciously. A man as proud as Justin would hate the fact that the knowledge of his unhappy first marriage was general, even if his emotions went no deeper than that. But he had loved Alison, at the beginning if not afterwards, so there must be pain, possibly guilt in his feelings. And she had twitted him with the knowledge, barbing her words to hurt as much as possible.

Whatever had been the situation after last night's episode, it was infinitely worse now. There could be no prospect of anything like friendship between them.

Perhaps it was better that way. As she put away the records they had used last night she admitted for the first time that she had come perilously close to falling in love with him—no, to loving him. She had fallen in love before, the last time with David, but mixed in with the desire Justin aroused in her was an emotion which could almost be love, if a yearning for his happiness above hers was love. Love for a man who was another woman's; and that woman her half-sister.

At least she had seen her folly in time. By antagonising Justin she had made certain there would be no further intimacy like that of the evening before, when his changed attitude had broken down her defences, putting her in such jeopardy that even now she could not think of it without a twist of desire deep within her. Much more of that companionable communion of mind and spirit, and she would be fathoms deep in love with him.

Some basic instinct told her that from this love there would be no escape, and freedom won only at the cost of tears and a desolation of spirit such as she had never before experienced.

So she could be very, very thankful that she had only fallen a little in love with him, and as soon as they were back in Auckland and she was working she would not have time to even think about what had so nearly happened. No doubt Justin was even now congratulating himself on not making any move towards her last night and vowing that he would never again find himself in such a fraught situation.

On which singularly bleak thought she did the bedrooms. A peep through his door showed that he had made his own bed, which relieved her of the chore of doing it for him.

It was with a sigh of relief that she heard the motorboat make its way into the bay in the late morning. Cherry and Rob would act as buffers, and with a little ingenuity there would be no need for her to be alone with Justin again.

But even they seemed to have suffered a change. Although superficially they seemed the same Linnet sensed that both were working hard to maintain their placid everyday attitudes.

It made for an odd, tense afternoon. The weather had cleared completely, and towards evening even the sea died down to its usual calmness, the waves crisping gently across the pale sand as Goori, relieved at the absence of the turmoil which had kept him firmly tucked away in the back of his kennel for the duration of the storm, galloped in a puppyish fashion after the cheeky gulls.

Rob had done some rapid tidying up around the garden, muttering to himself as he found another branch hanging loose, but rather relieved on the whole at the lack of damage. Even the marigolds had come through almost unscathed, they held up their gold and bronze and brown damascened blooms to the light, each one gay as a small sun.

The wind had caused some havoc in the orchard trees, knocking off small peaches and apples, but the tougher citrus fruit remained almost all intact. So Rob was happy.

So was Cherry. She sang as she prepared dinner; from where Linnet and Sarah pulled weeds in one of the garden beds they could hear her rich, warm voice drifting from pop songs to ones obviously learned at school, lingering over some, singing snatches of others.

'It sounds nice, doesn't it?' Sarah commented. 'I like it when you sing too, Linnet.'

'Do I sing?'

'Yes, just like Cherry, not really knowing you're doing it.' She heaved a particularly nasty weed forth, contemplated it with satisfaction, then flung it into the wheelbarrow, saying somewhat aloofly, 'My mummy used to sing me to sleep. I wasn't too young to remember.'

Linnet's heart contracted. Sarah had been only two when Alison died, but perhaps she could recall the sweetness of those moments before sleep.

'Mine too,' she said. 'A story, then a song.'

'Your mother wasn't your sister's mother, was she?'

'Sarah!'

Her father's voice made both of them jump guiltily, so hard with condemnation it was.

Without turning to look at him Linnet said lightly, 'No. Bronwyn is my half-sister.'

Doggedly, ignoring Justin, Sarah asked, 'So if Daddy got married again, I would have half-brothers and sisters?'

'If there were children, yes.' Linnet rubbed a hand across her forehead, leaving, no doubt, a great smudge of dirt behind. She could feel Justin as he stood behind her; it seemed that her very skin was sensitive to his presence. The conversation was a normal one for a child, so why was she so embarrassed, and why was Justin so angry?

Sarah lifted her head, looking at her father for the first time since his arrival, her expression tight with control.

'Then why don't you and Linnet get married, Daddy? I would like some sisters and brothers if Linnet was their mother.'

There was the oddest pause during which Linnet felt as if someone had hit her in the solar plexus, rendering her too winded even to feel embarrassment. Unseeingly she gazed at the sow-thistle she had just pulled, then with an effort, put it on to the pile beside her. Not for her life could she have got to her feet and confronted Justin.

Then he said, hateful amusement beneath the level tones, 'I've no doubt, honey, but you can't just marry people off to suit yourself, you know. I'm quite sure Linnet would have something to say about wishing such a fate on to her. She's got a career in mind.'

Perhaps it was just as well he was so sneeringly amused, for it brought the colour to Linnet's face as nothing else could have. Crisply he added, 'One of the toughest things about growing up is that you discover that life isn't like one of your favourite stories, Sarah. All the ends aren't tidied up neatly on the last page.'

Sarah had gone white, then red. Now her eyes filled with tears as she wailed, 'But I want you to get married! I hate——'

'*Sarah!*'

The cold ferocity of Justin's voice made the child gulp, knuckling her eyes with a desperation which tore Linnet's heart.

But regardless of her butter-soft heart, for the child's sake she couldn't come over all maternal.

'Here's a hanky,' she said quietly, scrambling to her feet.

When Sarah had buried her face into the handkerchief Linnet looked across at Justin, bracing herself for the condemnation she was certain would be in his glance.

Instead she met the most expressionless of looks. A cool, sweeping scrutiny which left her feeling flayed, as if he had seen right into her innermost being. Then he jerked his head, banishing her, and as she crunched her way up the shelly path she could hear his voice, lowered so that the words were indistinguishable.

Just before a large hibiscus bush marked a turn in the path she turned, saw him with his arm around his daughter, her fair head tucked under his chin as he lifted her. A desolation so intense it took her completely by surprise swamped her in a merciless wave, leaving her shaken and cold in the sunlight.

Perhaps it was at that moment that she realised that those two people were the dearest in the world to her, dearer even than her own mother, far dearer than anyone she had ever loved before.

Completely knocked off balance by this knowledge, she found herself heading for a secluded little nook beneath an enormous jacaranda tree where someone had had the happy idea of putting a table and two loungers so that they overlooked a thick swirl of vegetation and between two trees, a glimpse of the sea, now the blue of a Madonna's robe, so different from its angry viciousness of yesterday. The feathery shade of the tree cooled her as she sank on to the cushions of the lounger, but it could not cool the raging fires of the emotions which swirled within her.

As she always did when confronted by something new she endeavoured to face the thing squarely, but could only ask herself how she had managed to fall in love with someone like Justin, so cold and withdrawn, so aloof, the very opposite of any man she had ever loved before. Like David—how far away and futile her love for him seemed now!—they had all been gentle and considerate, friends rather than lovers, kind rather than passionate. Perhaps David had been right and she had sought a father when she had thought she wanted a lover. About as big a contrast to Justin Doyle as anyone could be, she thought drearily. He just wasn't her type! She had never felt at ease with men who had walked in an aura of blatant sexuality, although her honesty compelled her to admit she had never before met anyone who had anything like Justin's attraction. She didn't even like handsome men, normally! And certainly not a creature who resembled nothing so much as flint, hard and cold, with the ability to strike sparks off any woman he cared to impress.

And yet she loved him, irrevocably, oceans deep, mountains high, loved him with a fervour which made any other experience she had had like the flickering of a hearth fire before the searing, killing flash of the lightning.

Ruthlessly she brought her love into the clear light of the sun, searching to see if it could be just lust, the need of her young body for passion to slake a hunger she had never appreciated before. To be sure, her need for Justin was urgent; when Sarah had spoken of her bearing his children she had been overwhelmed by a primitive surge of passion at the vision she had had, of lying in his arms.

But that was not all. There was more than a hunger of the senses. She wanted so much more than to be his lover; she wanted to share his life, to talk with him, to make him happy.

Something her mother had said once came into her mind. 'Love is when you want your lover's happiness more than your own,' Jennifer had murmured, angry at a book she had read. 'This book is about *passion*, not love. It cheapens everything, makes it a matter of "I want, I need——" Love is when you're comrades as well as lovers, and when you think of the other's happiness before your own.'

Well, it seemed highly unlikely that she and Justin could ever be comrades, but Linnet knew that given the right conditions it could have happened. Only once or twice had they discussed anything without animosity; she had enjoyed the stimulus that his keen brain gave her and knew that she had held her own.

But then Bronwyn could give him that, and passion too.

At the thought of her sister Linnet sprang to her feet impelled by an urge for action, anything to get away from the unpalatable fact that there was little or no difference between her feelings for Justin and Bronwyn's.

The thought was so odious that she could not bear it, and went running up to the house as if hell itself lay behind her.

'I've been looking for you,' came a reproachful voice from just inside the door. 'Would you like to go for a swim? Daddy said we're going back tomorrow morning.'

'Are we?' Thank God, her brain said, but her heart wept. 'Yes, I'd like to swim.'

'We've got an hour before tea.'

The nearest thing was a scarlet bikini, but it had to be covered with a wrap before she ran with Sarah down to the beach. Once there they played a while together, then Linnet left her charge building a castle on the beach and struck out for the other side of the bay, seeking to exhaust herself in the rhythm of her stroke, to clear her mind of everything but the water and the sun and the physical sensations of her body.

She was a good swimmer, strong and fast, and made the other side with no difficulty. Once there she waved to Sarah, then began the return journey.

Halfway back a searing pain caught her in the leg, forcing a cry between her lips. For a moment she couldn't breathe, held in thrall by the agony, then she found herself spluttering as she sank beneath the water, and after that there was a nightmare of pain and fear which made her thrash out in a useless effort to keep her head above water.

How long it was before she was hauled to the surface again she never knew; probably only a minute or so, for later she discovered that Justin had been in the water before she went under. But it wasn't until she was back on the sand, had had the water in her lungs forcibly expelled and been sick, that she realised just how close she had been to death.

And then, in the face of Sarah's terrified silence and Justin's grim efficiency, she had to fight off the bout of sobbing in case she frightened the child even further. But the tears filled her eyes and flowed down her cheeks, and her breath came heavily, in short gasps which hurt her chest and ribs.

'Are you all right?' Sarah enquired in a high, thin voice. 'Linnet, are you all right now?'

'Leave her,' Justin ordered. 'She's fine, sweetheart. Look, colour is coming back into her cheeks.'

And so saying he swung her up into his arms and

carried her up to the house with Sarah trotting anxiously behind.

Linnet found she was crying quietly, the tears dripping down on to his chest, each soft gasping breath releasing more as she relaxed against the warm strength of his arms and shoulders. Once she made an effort to wipe them away, but he said in dry tones, 'You can't make me any wetter than I am already,' and she just let them flow.

Half an hour later she was tucked up in bed, the electric blanket on and Sarah gone, shooed from the room by Cherry, who, unflappable as ever, had known exactly what to do.

And then the tears came properly, so that she wept bitterly for the ache in her heart, wept as if she was releasing herself from all the pain which lay ahead.

After a while she slept.

It must have been after midnight when she woke, for the house was quiet, and a glance from the window showed that the McCarthys' cottage was dark and still. Very quietly she crawled from beneath the bedclothes, surprised to find that someone had been in and turned off the electric blanket. She was a little stiff and sore, but apart from that felt well and ravenously hungry.

So, with the least possible amount of noise, she pulled a thin cotton wrap on over her transparent nightgown and made her way to the door, waiting there with bated breath. There was no noise but the almost silent hush of the waves, no sound of anyone moving, so she tiptoed down the passage towards the kitchen.

Once there she closed the door behind her; fortunately it clicked only once, and that softly. Without switching the light on she made her way across to the fridge. If anything had been left over from dinner it would be stored there.

In the silence the faint rattle of the door seemed ominously loud; she looked anxiously over her shoulder for a moment, but there was no answering noise to indicate that she had woken anybody.

Unfortunately the interior light showed only the raw

materials of future meals; nothing remotely edible. So, again holding her breath, she closed the door and made her way across to where a large cane basket held an assortment of fruit.

An apple and a pear in either hand, she was half way back across the kitchen when to her horror she saw the door into the hall gape open. From the darkness of the passage Justin moved, panther-silent, into the room.

Certain that the heavy thumping of her heart must reverberate through the house, Linnet froze. Like a guilty Eve she clutched the fruit beneath her breasts as he came towards her, while her dry throat refused to allow any sound through.

'What the *hell* are you doing?' he breathed as he came up to within a few inches of her.

She couldn't prevent the step backwards. 'I'm hungry,' she managed, after licking her lips, 'so I got some fruit.'

Even in the darkness she could see his frown. 'I thought you were burgling the place.'

'You shouldn't have walked straight into the room, then,' she returned, striving for a touch of lightness. 'I could have bopped you from behind the door.'

'I'd already looked in your room, so I knew it was you,' he told her drily. 'Why didn't you turn the lights on?'

'I didn't want to wake anyone.'

'I'm a very light sleeper, but I'm more likely to wake at anything unusual, like someone tiptoeing around.'

'What about Sarah?'

The light through the window was quite strong, for she saw him smile, even saw the irony in it. 'If you stood by her bed and screamed into her ear she just might wake.'

'Oh.' She felt foolish, caught like a child stealing food, yet on edge too. Standing so close together and talking in whispers was an open invitation to intimacy. So she walked across to the sink and pressed the switch which brought the light above it to life.

Without looking behind her she pulled a door open, took out a glass and filled it with water to ease the dryness of her throat.

'Well, thank you for checking up on me,' she said politely, after she had drunk half of it. 'I'll eat the fruit in my bedroom.'

'Don't let me chase you out,' he returned, just as politely. 'Would you like some hot milk to go with it?'

'No, thank you.'

'No after-effects?'

'No, thank you.'

A moment of silence, then he asked silkily, 'Just what were you doing out in the middle of the bay?'

'Trying to drown,' she returned with a flippancy she was far from feeling. 'I'm sorry.'

'So I should bloody well think!'

At the barely repressed fury in his tones she turned, bewildered by the fact that Justin, who never swore, had twice sworn at her.

'Heavens, I didn't mean to,' she began spiritedly, 'I got cramp and——'

'Anyone with an atom of sense would have realised that swimming in a pool where the water is warm is no training for swimming a mile in the sea.' He bit the words out, each one cold condemnation. 'Sarah was almost out of her mind when I got you back!'

Linnet trembled. 'I am sorry,' she whispered, remembering the stark terror in the child's eyes.

'Sorry?' His hand shot out, fastened on her upper arm like a vice-grip, uncaring of the fact that he hurt her. 'I should hope so! Another death would have been more than she could have borne.'

'Another death?'

'Yes.' Those pale eyes were fixed on hers now, and she could see that he hated her. 'Sarah was with her mother when she rolled the car,' he told her with pitiless clarity. 'Alison wasn't wearing a seat belt and she was thrown under the car and crushed. She was still alive when I got her out, but she died almost immediately. Sarah saw her.'

CHAPTER SEVEN

A tide of nausea robbed Linnet's already pale face of whatever colour it had. With a curious repellant gesture she wiped her hand across her mouth as though by so doing she could wipe away Justin's words from her consciousness.

Poor little Sarah! It was no use telling herself that the child would not remember; an event like that would be deeply burned into her memory. No wonder she had panicked when she saw Linnet's struggles; no wonder Justin's features were set in an expression of implacable dislike!

'I didn't know,' she said beneath her breath. 'I'm sorry.'

Knocked off balance by the shock of this information, she lost any desire she might have had to answer him with her usual spirit. Instead, great tears welled up, drowning the gold in her eyes.

'I'm sorry,' she said again, knowing as she said it how useless such an apology was, but unable to think of anything else to say which would tell him how much she regretted opening old wounds for both him and his daughter.

'Stop that!' The words cracked like a whip in the still air.

Horrified, she blinked the tears back, but it was too late. Justin's other hand closed on to the softness of her shoulder as he jerked her into his arms and covered her trembling mouth with his own, kissing her with a kind of desperation which sent a warning signal to her brain before the sheer physical magic of his touch got through to her, and all of her fears were banished by the riotous response he awoke in her.

His mouth was firm and warm, weaving a spell to enthrall her senses. The warmth of his body radiated through her flimsy clothes, trembling faintly with the force of his desire. Linnet knew a traitorous surge of passion in response.

Then he lifted his head and kissed her eyes closed and his hands moved over to stroke the vulnerable nape of her neck beneath her hair, the other to hold her across the back. Perhaps he thought she wanted to pull away. Linnet was too lost in the primitive need to continue this delight to even think of moving from the warm haven of his arms; every warning of her brain was swamped.

Her skin tingled with anticipation as his mouth moved to her cheek and the lobe of an ear, the warm hollow beneath and down to the tender, throbbing base of her throat.

'Justin,' she whispered achingly.

'Hush!' One hand pushed the neck of her wrap back, revealing the skin beneath. Shivering at the smooth sensuous movement of his fingers across her skin, she must have made some soft noise, for he whispered again, 'Hush!'

The words were soft on her skin. Held in a trance of turbulence, at the mercy of needs and desires she could no longer control, Linnet lay quietly in his arms. Passion flared into life within her, an all-encompassing flame which responded to the hunger in him with the ardour of her generous youth.

Again she whispered his name, only to have it crushed to nothing beneath the pressure of his lips on her open mouth.

Ah, but she wanted him, wanted him, with a yearning which was as strong as it was lawless, conjured to life by his desire for her. He did not shock her, not even when his hands touched her body as if she were already his woman, for his hands and lips told her that she was beautiful, that he needed the soft forgetfulness of her skin, the willing nirvana of her body.

The distant sound of Sarah's voice was shocking in its suddenness, shocking in its effect on Linnet. It was a douche of icy water, a swift descent from rapture to cold sanity awakening her brain.

'Stay here,' Justin ordered harshly, shaking her as she turned blindly away from him. '*Stay here!*'

As coolly as if this had happened a hundred times before he collected a glass of water, threw a glance at her from which all of the glazed languor of passion had fled, and left the room.

Like a sleepwalker Linnet picked up the half empty glass of water she had left and drank, staring with distaste at the apple and the pear on the bench. An hysterical bubble of laughter had to be repressed; she did not feel at all hungry now. Ignoring them, and Justin's command, she switched the light off and made her way along the passage to her own bedroom.

But outside the door she paused, irresolute. Sarah was half-sobbing, and above Justin's deep tones Linnet could hear the childish voice calling her name.

Swiftly she went into Sarah's room.

'Oh, L-Linnet——' The wailing stopped. 'I had a horrid dream. I thought you were dead!'

'Well, as you can see, I'm not,' Linnet said in as matter-of-fact tones as she could manage with Justin's gaze on her. 'I'm sorry I gave you such a fright, chicken, but I'm fine now.'

She sat down as she spoke, on the opposite side of the bed from Justin, and received Sarah's clinging arms around her neck with a hug and a kiss on the flushed cheek.

'Silly old thing,' she soothed comfortably. 'Everything's fine now. Sh-sh!'

The sobbing stopped as if by magic. Whatever realms of fantasy and horror Sarah had inhabited had been banished well and truly.

'Daddy said you were asleep,' she said with a final hug before sliding back on to her pillows with a satisfied, sleepy smile. 'I'm sorry I woke you up.' Her half-closed eyes opened. 'We're like a family again, aren't we?' she said, only half smiling. 'Goodnight, Linnet. Goo'night, Daddy.'

Linnet retreated in as good order as she could; she almost ran into her bedroom and found herself staring around it as if in search of something to barricade the door. Scolding herself for being stupid she walked across to the window, drew back the curtain and stared out at the enormous stars caught in the black tangle of the silhouetted pines. A soft breeze brought the sound of the sea to her ears, carrying with it a faint salt scent mingled with the tang of pine tree balsam and a more exotic, heavier perfume from one of the shrubs.

A night made for love, she thought bitterly. Lord, what an *idiot* she had been! And thank God that little Sarah had had her nightmare. Probably set off by the faint noise of movement in the house, and how fortunate it had been for Linnet's chastity.

A slight noise made her swing to face the door, a hand flying to the pulse at the base of her throat as she saw Justin's silhouette in the opening. A rising tide of excitement had to be subdued as her head and her body fought for supremacy.

Striving for normality, she asked, 'Is she all right?'

'Yes, she's asleep again.'

In spite of his lowered tones she could hear that his voice was once more clear and cold with no trace of the thick smoothness of before.

'Good.'

He didn't move. Neither did Linnet. It was being made quite clear to her that if she went one step towards him she would no longer be able to call her soul—or her body—her own. And she could think of no worse fate for anyone than to love Justin and be his mistress.

After a moment of stressful silence she said flatly, 'I'm glad.'

'I thought you would be.' He moved then, and came towards her.

Linnet retreated to behind the chair. 'No——' she said thinly. 'No—I'm tired and——'

'Afraid,' he interrupted. 'Of me, Linnet?'

'Yes. And me,' she answered, her misery as obvious as her steadfastness.

There was a swift gleam of white as he smiled.

'Honest as ever! Will you wait a few minutes until you're certain she's asleep and then come along to my room? It's more comfortable than this.'

The calm effrontery hit her with a body blow. How *could* he, she thought numbly, how could he suggest such a thing?

'No!' Her voice matched his for iciness as she whipped up a torrent of hatred for him.

'Why not?' Reaching across the chair, he touched her throat, his thumb against the thin skin which could not hide the pulse beating there. 'Why not?' he asked again, almost without interest.

His touch was at once a caress and an intrusion. A pain in her bottom lip made Linnet conscious that she had been biting it—for how long?

'Because I don't want an affair with you,' she said huskily. Before her self-control deserted her she entreated, 'Justin, *please* go.'

He withdrew his hand, said unemotionally, 'Very well,' and turned and walked away.

Visited by the absurd fancy that he was walking out of her life for ever, Linnet found that her fists were clenched across her mouth to prevent herself from calling him back.

At the door he said, 'Goodnight, Linnet.'

'Goodnight.'

It was a brave effort, bravely delivered, and it was enough to convince him, for the door closed silently behind him as he left.

Like an automaton Linnet swung herself into bed, pulled the sheets over her and lay there, eyes wide in the darkness, as she realised with horror just how narrow an escape she had had from his practised seduction. Had

Sarah not called out that close embrace would have reached an inevitable conclusion, and Justin would have become her lover, privy to all of the secrets of her body, master of her heart and her life.

The images roused by this terrified her as much as they excited her. She could conceive of no greater happiness than to lie all night against his heart, but not because she happened to be the nearest available woman. Not even because he desired her. She wanted him to love her, and if the incident had done nothing else, it had revealed that she needed the commitment of marriage before she could give herself without guilt or shame. Making love should be a joyous affirmation of love and trust, not a snatched interlude which gratified only the needs of the body.

And you can't get more old-fashioned and romantic than that, she told herself, even as her strong sense of justice forced her to accept that what had happened had certainly not been all Justin's fault. To be sure, he had begun it, but after that first initial shock, he had received all the encouragement in the world.

Enough to make him think that she would be complaisant enough to go to his bedroom. Restlessly she turned and pummelled her pillow, bewildered as she often was, but this time with an underlay of pain, which was merely a continuation and strengthening of the pain she had felt for some time now.

What of Bronwyn? Somehow she could not believe that he would seduce his bride-to-be's sister, however driven by desire. He had standards, and principles. Surely he and Bronwyn could not be close enough for her sister to assume that marriage was almost inevitable?

One hand pressed to her aching head, Linnet fought with the jealousy this evoked, unable to make sense of the situation, except by thinking that Bronwyn had misread the relationship between her and Justin. And that was probably wishful thinking.

The only other alternative was one she found totally abhorrent, but she forced herself to face it. Perhaps Justin was the sort of man who saw nothing wrong in making love to the sister of the woman he intended to marry. If that was so, then she had fallen in love with a man who was no more than a figment of her imagination. And if that was so, she decided drearily, if Justin were as callous and lacking in principle as that, then it should be easy enough to fall out of love with him.

But oh, those moments in his arms had been sweet, a matchless magic of desire and rapture which had almost transcended the physical, lifting her into realms of the spirit, the existence of which she had never suspected.

At least he had given her that, even if he had spoiled it afterwards by the blunt sensuality of his request. In a way it was as well that he had been so hatefully practical, for he had forced her to see just how her behaviour appeared to him—as an open invitation to sex, unsoftened by anything like the love she felt.

'You still look washed out,' Sarah told her the next morning, gazing critically at her from the end of the bed. A sudden smile banished the solemnity of her expression. 'Well, you *were* washed out, weren't you? Washed out and washed up.'

If she could joke about it she was over the worst.

'Hardly,' Linnet told her banteringly. 'I think I look a bit tired because I was woken up in the middle of the night.'

'I haven't had a nightmare for ages,' Sarah confessed, coming to snuggle in beside her. 'Linnet, Cherry had a surprise for us last night.'

'And what was that?'

The fair head turned on Linnet's arm, the grey eyes so like her father's looked wistfully pleased. 'She's going to have a baby. Isn't she lucky?'

'Very.'

'She and Rob and Daddy drank champagne.' A heavy sigh. 'Linnet, would you marry Daddy if he asked you?'

Hoping that she betrayed nothing, Linnet answered

very tenderly, 'Darling, you must trust your father to pick out a nice new mother for you. It's not fair to him—or to me—to harp on this.'

Sarah sighed again, while a funny little smile touched her lips, making her look far more adult than her years. 'O.K., I won't, then, but I wish you would, Linnet. I don't want a new mother, I just want you.'

'I love you too. But loving doesn't always give you what you want.'

'I don't really know what you mean,' said Sarah, giving her a smack on the cheek before she scrambled out of the bed, 'but I suppose it's sensible. Linnet, what time is the plane coming?'

From outside came Cherry's voice, cheerful as ever yet with a deeper note of happiness which must be the direct result of her good news. 'At half past ten, so you'd better hop on out and have your breakfast, Miss Muffet. Your father is waiting.'

She was carrying a tray which she set down on the bedside table before standing back to regard Linnet with a faintly quizzical air.

'You still look a bit pale, but I daresay you'll do. Justin said you woke in the night.'

Oh, did he? With just as much emotion as he had said goodnight, no doubt, heartless autocrat!

'Yes,' and swiftly, 'Sarah tells me you celebrated last night. How lovely for you!'

Taking this for an invitation, Cherry sat down in the armchair. 'Isn't it? We'd almost given up hope, you know. Eat up, or it will get cold and I know you don't like cold toast.'

'Are you hoping for a boy or a girl—or don't you mind?' asked Linnet, buttering the toast so that Cherry shouldn't see the pain in her eyes.

'Oh, we don't mind!' Cherry laughed. 'I just hope it isn't the only one. I'd like a couple of kids; I don't think it does a kid good to be the only one. Look at young Sarah, such a funny, tense little thing, though she's improved a lot. Justin says it's all your doing.'

A treacherous warmth invaded Linnet's heart, but her innate honesty compelled her to say, 'I doubt it. She's taken a violent fancy to me, but I think it's only because I've taken an interest in her.'

'Yes. Anna has enough to do keeping the house tidy, of course. She's a bit of a fanatic that way. And although he loves her, Justin is a busy man. I think she's been looking for a substitute mother and hopes she's found one.'

Under Cherry's steady gaze Linnet felt her glance fall. Unconsciously she sighed, saying in a muffled voice, 'Poor little scrap! She wrings my heart, but I . . .'

Her voice drifted into silence as she looked up, appealing to the other woman's sturdy good sense.

'But you don't want to get too involved. I don't blame you. It is an awkward situation, isn't it?'

'More than that.' Linnet looked troubled, but did not feel inclined to unburden herself to Cherry, spoil her joyous day with other people's worries. So she smiled. 'Still, we'll see it through, and I'll do my best not to hurt Sarah.'

'Fair enough.' Cherry got to her feet. 'And eat everything up! I don't want you feeling squeamish half way to Auckland.'

Linnet applied herself to the toast with a will; possibly that was why she managed a somewhat bumpy trip back without any qualms except those of being close to Justin. A very aloof Justin, well entrenched behind that mask, the only flicker of emotion in his expression when he spoke to Sarah. To Linnet he was courteous, painfully so; she was equally polite while within her heart felt as though someone was twisting it into shreds.

Anna met them in the big car, relinquishing the wheel with an air of relief. She greeted Sarah with restrained affection, Linnet with something closer to a welcome than she had ever managed before. Perhaps in time she could get over that first occasion of their meeting and see Linnet as a perfectly ordinary person, no threat to anyone. Linnet hoped so.

Bronwyn was out. A note on the kitchen table informed

Linnet that she'd be back in the evening. Just that. Feeling rather forlorn, Linnet unpacked, changed into shorts, and opened windows, then picked some snapdragons and put them in a vase in the living room.

'Linnet? Do you want to come for a swim?'

After only a moment's hesitation Linnet called back, 'Yes. Come in, Sarah.'

She was less pleased when she found Justin by the pool, his lean length stretched out in a lounger in the shade of one of the big tree ferns which gave the pool such atmosphere.

And less pleased when after she had been in the water ten minutes he strolled over to the side of the pool, snapped his fingers at her as if summoning a dog and said laconically, 'Out.'

'I beg your pardon?' Pushing wet hair back from her face, she gaped at him.

A smile twitched his lips. 'You heard. You've been in long enough.'

As she made no move he went on blandly, 'You wouldn't want me to come in and get you, would you?'

There was no mistaking the meaning in his voice, or the way his eyes ran across the smooth line of her shoulders and breasts.

Linnet flushed, dived beneath the water and made her way across to the steps, furiously angry with him and with herself for being so easily intimidated.

When she emerged from the dressing room Sarah called out that she was doing her lengths, as Anna set a tray of drinks down on a table between Justin's lounger and another. After a quick word with Justin the housekeeper moved off towards the house and Justin poured two drinks.

'Come and sit down,' he commanded. 'You look a bit tired.'

Most emphatically Linnet did not want to share a drink with him, but she could not think of a suitably sophisticated way of getting out of it. Besides, she told herself, she was going to have to establish some sort of everyday relationship with him, and the longer she put it off the harder it was going to be.

So keeping her mind firmly on the prospect of a cool drink she sat down, wishing that he had chosen chairs rather than loungers. Stretched out like that her legs were very long and bare.

Justin seemed content to sit in silence, sipping the drink which Linnet discovered to be fruit juice, pleasantly cooled by ice blocks, with sprigs of lemon balm lending their aromatic tang. In the pool Sarah had given up lengths and was playing with a big inflated ball.

The silence stretched out, became hard to cope with. Linnet found herself prickling with tension. Impulsively she asked a question she had long been pondering.

'Justin, how well did you know my father?'

There was a short silence, during which she wondered if she had left herself open for a monumental snub.

Then he answered, 'As well as anyone towards the end of his life, I suppose. Why? Surely you're not feeling guilty this late in the day about your lack of interest in him?'

'There was no lack of interest.'

'Then why didn't you come to see him?'

The question was so manifestly unfair that she became indignant. 'How could I? Air fares cost money, and that was one thing we didn't have.'

'You got here when you wanted to.'

The censure in his tones brought her immediately on to the defensive. 'A one-way ticket took almost all of my savings. I'm living on the rest.'

'Your father sent an adequate amount to live on.'

'I don't know anything about the financial arrangements.' With a shaking hand she picked up her drink, sipped some, then with some slight gain in composure said, 'Look, leave it. I'm sorry I asked.'

She sensed rather than saw the swift lift of his shoulders. 'I would have thought that Bronwyn was able to tell you more than I.'

'I said it doesn't *matter*!' Astounded by the sharp note

in her voice, she swung her legs down on to the ground, prepared to get up and run, regardless of what he thought.

But his hand caught her wrist, held her still with merciless strength as he said quietly, 'Sit down.'

As she attempted to rise he jerked her down, repeating on a note of warning, 'Sit down, Linnet. I'm not going to eat you.'

When she was back on the lounger she watched as the white marks left by his fingers filled in and knew that there would be bruises there tomorrow.

'Your father was a disappointed man,' he began conversationally. 'He didn't speak much of his life, but I gathered that he had never got over your mother's defection. On rare occasions he spoke of you, with great affection. Both he and Bronwyn missed you intensely.'

I wonder why, his tone implied. Linnet swallowed, asking huskily, 'But what was he like?'

'What do you remember of him?'

She hesitated, then decided that honesty was the only policy. 'Very little. He left early for work, and when he came home he spent most of his time in the study. Once or twice he came to my birthday parties, but usually he was working.' She went on with a flash of spirit, 'I remember my mother crying, often, but very little of my father.'

'He said you were small and dainty, a little redheaded fairy with an enchanting smile. He was right about the smile.'

Totally astounded, Linnet turned her head, met a derisive smile and felt pain and anger war for supremacy. Anger won. Icily she retorted, 'Is that all he said? He didn't know me particularly well, did he, to forget to mention the strong mercenary streak.'

'I can understand that,' he said coolly, 'if you've always been short of money. Possibly you feel entitled to half of the estate. What's happening about that now?'

Fairly caught, cursing her too-ready tongue, she could only say foolishly, 'The lawyers are still working on it.'

'It's not too late to pull out, even now. Unless you really do feel that you're entitled to it.'

Of course, he would want Bronwyn to get what she wanted. The sun turned Linnet's hair into a nimbus of red-gold as she bent her head away from his too intent gaze.

'I don't know,' she said after a while. 'It's none of your business, anyway, Justin. Leave it, will you? You still haven't told me much about my father.'

His withdrawal was palpable. 'There's very little to tell. An intelligent man, with Bronwyn's dry sense of humour. He lived for his work. I liked him.'

'Did you?'

'Yes. He was an honest man who didn't pretend.'

Linnet did not like the sarcastic inflection of the last sentence, but she ignored it. Let him think what he liked! Thanks to Bronwyn he had always had a pretty low opinion of her; the events at Kawau could only have strengthened it. No doubt he thought her wanton as well as mercenary and hard-hearted because she wouldn't give up her job for Sarah.

Then Sarah arrived, demanding a drink, and sat down on the lounger by Linnet's feet, enjoying the sweet fruit juice with noisy appreciation. A few minutes of conversation ensued, until at last Linnet got up, relieved at the prospect of escaping from Justin's critical presence.

Even then Sarah wanted her to come up for dinner, turning petulant when she refused.

'Why not?' she demanded crossly.

'Because she said not,' Justin told her with just enough authority to quieten her.

And Linnet left, feeling that she had been exposed to more than any one person should ever have to endure.

Bronwyn arrived in at about ten o'clock, smartly casual in jeans and a denim jacket, carrying her beautiful hand-made boots in her hand with rueful care.

'Look at that!' she greeted Linnet without preamble. 'You wouldn't think there'd be so much mud around anywhere, would you?'

'Where on earth have you been?'

The older girl managed to look both secretive and amused. 'Up the coast a bit.'

'Oh.' Somewhat deflated by this cavalier greeting, Linnet asked, 'Would you like something to drink?'

'Coffee would be delicious.'

When it was made she sat on the sofa, lashes hiding the blue depths of her eyes as she sipped. 'How did your week go?'

'Fine. The weather was lovely until it broke.'

'Did you cope with Sarah?'

'Yes.' Linnet hesitated, before saying, 'She's a dear little soul, really. She just needs someone to love her.'

Her sister yawned, but not before there was, Linnet could have sworn, another flash of amusement in her eyes. 'No doubt. Losing your mother at an early age doesn't do much for your stability—look at me. Oh, by the way, there's another letter from your mama over on the table—did you see it?'

'Yes, I did.'

An oddly stilted conversation. After a minute or so during which Bronwyn surveyed her hands with an air of satisfaction she asked, 'What will you do when I move out of here?'

Linnet felt a throb of pain deep within, but she answered with composure, 'Find myself a flat, or board with someone. Why?'

'I just wondered. How much are you likely to earn as a librarian? Congratulations, by the way.'

When Linnet had told her she frowned, obviously working something out. 'You'll have to share a flat; you'll never be able to afford one on your own.'

'Are you planning on going soon?'

Bronwyn dazzled her with her smile. 'Fairly soon, but don't tell anyone yet. It's still a secret.'

Which meant—what? That she and Justin had already set the date for their marriage? Somehow Linnet could not believe it. Yet what else should make Bronwyn so confident? There had been no other man in her life since

Linnet had arrived, so it had to be Justin.

Setting her cup down, she said hollowly, 'I think I'll go to bed. Goodnight.'

'I'll see you in the morning.'

The telephone rang as Linnet went through the door into her room. She stopped, looked back and listened as Bronwyn answered. 'Why, hallo! Yes—well, yes, she's just going. Oh!' The older girl swivelled to survey her sister. 'Did she, indeed? That must be why she looks so tired. Yes, Justin, I'll pack her off to bed straight away. Goodnight—and thank you.'

When the receiver had gone down she said accusingly, 'You twit! Trying to drown yourself like a kid with no sense! What on earth would your mother have had to say if Justin hadn't been there!'

'Well, he was,' Linnet said peaceably, her sore heart soothed by the knowledge of Justin's anxiety.

Bronwyn came across to stand before her, small, somehow indomitable in spite of her size. In a totally unexpected gesture she took Linnet's hand and squeezed it, saying as she released her, 'You're a darling, aren't you? That mother of yours must have something to have brought you up so well. Do you think she'd come if I invited her to my wedding?'

'I'm sure she would,' Linnet answered, feeling the bottom of her world drop out from beneath her.

'Good. I'd like to make peace. Life's too short to hold grudges.' Bronwyn lifted her brows in faint surprise. 'I've only just discovered that. Must be love's influence. Wonderful thing, ain't it?'

Linnet smiled, then went into her room and closed the door behind her, wishing she could cry so that her tears would dissolve the hard, heavy lump in her chest which was making it so difficult to breathe.

There was no hope now. Bronwyn would not speak so casually of her wedding if it were not a foregone conclusion, so the arrangements must be in hand. Which meant that Justin was all that she had hoped he wouldn't be—a philanderer with no moral sense, who could see no wrong in trying to seduce one woman when engaged to another.

Linnet tried to tell herself that she was better off without him, but while her head agreed her heart and body formed an active fifth column, weakening her praiseworthy determination to cut him from her life by their constant yearning.

The next few days were grim. Linnet found her appetite had gone; at mealtimes she had to force food down, thankful that Bronwyn seemed too busy with her own affairs to take much notice of her sister's. Indeed, something had happened to Bronwyn. It would be overstating the case to say that she was radiant, for her emotions had been kept in restraint for so long that she could not reveal them as openly as other people. But she was certainly happy, while trying to hide it with an approximation of her usual blasé manner, and failing.

Of Justin Linnet saw nothing, for which she was thankful. She felt she could not bear to meet him ever again.

But the weather was wet, as gloomy as Linnet's outlook; Sarah developed into a little ghost, haunting her footsteps. Fortunately they discovered a book which had all sorts of exciting things to do, and before long Sarah's bedroom table was strewn with all sorts of bits and pieces while she was initiated into the excitements of French knitting and candle bulldozers, plaiting raffia belts and making mobiles. Between them they even made a lampshade of brightly coloured wool for Anna's birthday.

It was during these miserable days that Linnet discovered that the housekeeper's attitude had softened even more into something very like friendship.

One day she brought an afternoon snack into the room, tea for Linnet and fruit juice for Sarah, and instead of leaving as she usually did, drew up a chair and sat down, listening with a smile while Sarah showed her their projects.

'You've made a difference to that one,' she said when Sarah disappeared for a moment. 'She used to be a whining, miserable little thing, demanding everyone's attention all the time. She nearly drove me out of my mind!'

Linnet repressed the desire to point out that all that the child had needed was someone's attention and love. Anna had never had children, so it was unfair to expect her to know how to cope. It did not occur to her that the same might be said of her.

Instead she murmured, 'We started off on the right foot. This hero-worshipping attitude won't last, of course.'

Anna looked unconvinced. 'We used to have a nurse for her, but she left to get married when Sarah went to school. She stood no nonsense, but the child was fond of her. And of course she's always been devoted to her father, but he's away for most of the day. She needs a mother.'

Well, she would be having one soon; surely out of the depths of her own happiness Bronwyn could spare some for Sarah. Aloud, Linnet replied, 'I suppose she does.'

'She missed her own mother dreadfully, poor little scrap. I remember when Justin brought her home; she lay like a little ghost, white as a sheet, didn't eat, didn't talk for days. They were very close, those two.'

'Justin and Sarah?'

'Well, yes, but I meant his wife—Alison—and Sarah.' Anna pursed her lips. 'She wasn't much of a wife, poor thing, but she did her best for Sarah, I'll say that for her.'

A question trembled on Linnet's lips, but she bit it back. It was not fair to tempt Anna to gossip, and what on earth use would it be for her to learn any more about poor Alison? She knew that Sarah's mother could not possibly have committed suicide as Stewart had implied. No fond mother would have tried to kill herself with her small daughter strapped in the car beside her.

Oddly enough this was a relief. It had hurt to think that Justin could have been cruel enough to drive his wife to take her own life. Arrogant and heartless he might be, but at least he did not have that sin on his soul.

Sarah's return put an end to any more confidences, but it was to be an afternoon of interruptions, for much later Stewart strolled in, dropped a parcel on the table before

Sarah and stood back to watch her reaction with amusement.

'What is it?' Sarah breathed, unwrapping it as carefully as if it had been a jewelled casket from fabled lands.

'Have a look.'

'Oh! Another Paddington Bear book! Oh, Uncle Stewart, you are a *dear*! How did you know there was another one out?'

He received her rapturous hug with equanimity. 'I keep my eyes and ears to the ground, missy. What have you been up to here?'

'I'm making a mobile—see, these are baby ducks and this is the mother. We have to sew the felt ones and the foam plastic one together—Linnet showed me how. When it's finished I'm going to put it above my bed.'

'Clever girl! And clever Linnet too.'

He sat down and to Linnet's astonishment did two very neat blanket stitches, then looked up, eyes gleaming with challenging laughter at her expression.

'And clever Stewart,' he mocked her. 'Hear you had a nasty experience at Kawau, Linnet.'

'Yes,' she replied, unwilling even now to remember those moments of panic beneath the sea.

'You look as though you haven't got over it yet. You can overdo the eye make-up put on with a smutty finger, you know.'

When he had gone Sarah put her head on one side, announcing, 'Uncle Stewart has changed.'

'Oh?'

'Yes. He used to be—funny; nice, but as if he didn't want you to know it. And he argued with Daddy. But he doesn't now. I think,' nodding her head portentously, 'I think something has happened to him.'

Perhaps he's been released from bondage, Linnet thought frivolously, sorry for Stewart who seemed to be yet another poor fool yearning for the unattainable. In his case a way of life, the farm Rob said he wanted. In her case, a man who wasn't worth it.

Justin wasn't returning home until late that night, so

when Sarah begged her to stay for dinner Linnet agreed, running down through the warm rain to leave a note for Bronwyn. Stewart also was out, so they ate in the kitchen with Anna, and whether it was in reaction to the weather or just an excess of high spirits, they were all very giggly and frivolous.

Surprising, Linnet thought, that you could laugh and joke and tease when your heart was breaking.

Then Sarah had her bath, and Linnet told her a story; by now her bedtime tales had become a saga about the lives of a group of *turehu*, fairy people who lived in the misty, bushclad hills in the old days. When, kissed and tucked up, the child had dropped off to sleep Linnet enjoyed a cup of tea with Anna in front of the television set.

An unfortunate diversion, as it happened, for Justin walked in on them just as Anna was clearing away the teacups, and insisted on escorting Linnet back to the flat in spite of her protests.

The rain had eased to a light spotty drizzle, so that there was no need of coat or umbrella. Overhead the occasional star shone bravely through the heavy slow-moving clouds, promise of fine weather on the morrow. The air was fresh, fragrant with the spicy scent of flowers and greenery released by the rain. Beside Linnet Justin was silent, but he held her arm firmly, for she had tripped going through the back door.

It was an odd, short walk, fraught with a tension which made Linnet's skin prickle with anticipation, even as she told herself that the last thing Justin was likely to do was make any move towards her.

Lights glowed dully through the drawn curtains of the flat. Bronwyn could have only the lamp on. Faintly the stereo could be heard in the living room. Neil Diamond, by the sound of it, one of Bronwyn's favourites.

When they reached the garage Linnet said hurriedly, 'Thank you for coming down with me. I'll be fine now.'

'I'll come in with you.'

Recognising that voice, she inserted the key into the lock, walked across the darkened dining room and into the sitting room.

To see Bronwyn and Stewart locked in the sort of embrace about which there could be no misunderstanding.

CHAPTER EIGHT

LINNET's first impulse was to turn and make her way out of the room, sweeping Justin with her so that he did not see the two lost in their own world behind her. Whether she wanted to save Bronwyn from the consequences of this folly, or whether it was Justin she wanted to protect she could never afterwards decide.

Whatever it was, it was too late. Justin's hand was on her shoulder, gripping with an intensity which threatened to crack the bones. Perhaps one of them made a small sound, for Stewart removed his lips from Bronwyn's, looked up, and flushed a dull red.

'We've got an audience, darling,' he said, pulling her around so that she could button up her blouse in some sort of privacy.

Linnet felt a singing in her ears, swallowed and said numbly, 'I'll—I'll go and put the kettle on.'

But Justin's cruel grip kept her still until Stewart came towards them, the challenging light very bright in his eyes, his features set in a stubborn mould which made his resemblance to Justin much stronger.

'No need to go, Linnet. You'd have known fairly soon anyway, both of you. Bronwyn and I are getting married.'

There was a hint of defiance in his voice, but a strength of purpose which was stronger, and the glance which he sent in their direction was every bit as compelling as anything Justin could summon up.

Good for you, Linnet found herself saying in delighted surprise. Relief seeped through her entire being as Justin's grip loosened on her shoulder, to be replaced immediately by remorseful solicitude. She had never thought she would feel sorry for him, but it had happened and she could only wish that he was as unaffected as he outwardly appeared to be.

Then he propelled her further into the room, saying with a hint of dryness but no other inflection in his voice, 'Congratulations, and felicitations, Bronwyn.'

Bronwyn had risen from the sofa, pale, yet just as determined as Stewart. Her glance flickered across Linnet's startled face, met Justin's steady, emotionless gaze and she smiled.

'Thank you.'

There followed an odd ten minutes, strained in spite of everyone's superb good manners, before Justin and Stewart left together.

'Well?' The word was tossed off as a challenge.

Linnet gave her sister a sudden, fervent hug. 'I hope you'll be *very* happy,' she said warmly.

Her sister's soft chuckle was wry. 'So do I.'

'Are you sure?'

'Stop looking so anxious. I'm sure.' She sat down on the sofa, once more the cool, hard-to-decipher Bronwyn in spite of the softer light which gleamed behind those heavy white lids. 'Stewart and I are not *ingénues*, demanding heavenly fulfilment from any relationship, but this time I think we both might come out winners.'

'But—Justin!'

Bronwyn smiled, a rather sardonic smile. 'That's been off for a while. Never was on, to tell the truth, in spite of all my hopes.'

Thunderstruck was about the most appropriate way to describe Linnet's feelings. 'But when I came here—and that's not very long ago as weeks go—you told me you were marrying him!'

'Wishful thinking. It was Stewart even then, but I refused to face it. Do you remember the night you and Justin took Sarah to the firework display?'

'Yes.' Of course. It sometimes seemed that she remembered every minute of her life since she first set eyes on Justin.

'He came down that night, and we had a fight. Not just my usual sniping, but a good, honest no-holds-barred

fight. I called him everything under the sun and he re-
taliated with some choice epithets of his own. I slapped
his face, and he kissed me.' She stopped, smiling at
Linnet's horrified expression. 'All very vulgar, but it did
the trick.'

'But you still went out with Justin after that.'

'I wouldn't admit my feelings for a while. And really,
my dear, my dates with Justin have always been pretty
platonic. The passion is there, but he kept it well leashed,
even when I was full of enthusiasm.' She shrugged, as if
the thought of that eagerness was distasteful to her. 'He's
a cunning devil. He knew what I was after, but being the
experienced, worldly man he is he let me down lightly, I
suppose. I don't really care now. He excited me, but it
was the glamour I was in love with, not the man.'

Linnet should have been relieved, should even have
been happy, but she was not. After all, she had always
sensed that Justin did not love Bronwyn. And it would be
the height of naïvety to think that because he did not
want to marry Bronwyn—and she had only Bron's word
for that—there was any hope for her.

Aloud she asked, 'Are you sure that you'll be happy
with Stewart, Bron?'

'Nothing's sure but death, little sister, but I think we'll
manage. He's leaving the business and I'm selling the
boutique and we're buying a farm north of Auckland. We
looked at it the day you came back from Kawau. It's
close enough to a country centre so that if I get bored
being a wife and mother I can open another shop.'

'And his drinking?'

Bronwyn laughed. 'We won't have enough money for
him to buy booze, or enough time for him to drink it.'
With an abrupt change of mood she said seriously, 'He's
been unhappy. I can make sure that he's happy; I hope
that will do the trick.'

'I hope so too. When are you getting married?'

'In a month or so. I'll write to your mum and ask her.
Or would you rather I didn't? Because of her new
spouse?'

Linnet looked faintly astonished. 'David? Gosh no, I've
got over him ages ago.' A pity it had to be accomplished
by putting someone else in his place, someone who was so
vivid and virile in her life that he made David seem a
pale wraith from the past.

Conscious that Bronwyn had bent her shrewd glance
on her she continued with spirit, 'I can assure you, David
is nothing to me now.'

'Good.' Stretching luxuriously across the sofa, Bronwyn
smiled, a slow, rather secretive smile which gave her all of
the allure of the old Nile, a modern Cleopatra with her
fascinating trick of half-lowering her eyelids and looking
out from beneath them as she was doing now. 'You know,
you look a bit washed out. I'd wear a liquid base to cover
up those circles under your eyes if I were you. And you'd
better get off to bed. I feel a bit tired myself. In a way
I'm rather glad you and Justin happened on us, it saved a
lot of explanations.'

'It certainly did,' Linnet agreed fervently.

Bronwyn laughed, and after a moment Linnet joined
her.

'You should have seen your face,' the older girl said
after a moment. 'Sheer shock personified!'

'And Justin?'

Again that penetrating glance. 'Oh, he retired behind
that mask of his,' Bronwyn replied lightly. 'Whenever
someone mentions a graven image I think of Justin. But
take my word for it, he's not heartbroken. By the way,
when are you going to see your librarian?'

'I thought tomorrow.'

'Good idea. You're starting after new year, aren't you?'

'Yes.' By then Bronwyn would be married and there
would be no reason for Linnet to be at the flat.

'Mm. Do you need money?'

Shaking her head, Linnet said firmly, 'No. I've
enough. David and Mum sent me a bank draft and that
will keep me until I start work.'

'When you'll start paying them back, of course.'

'Well, yes.'

'All the virtues, independence being one of them, Eiluned Grant. Some man is going to have trouble with you!'

Linnet wondered if her expression was as stricken as her heart at these half-joking words. Perhaps she did reveal some of the emotion holding her in thrall, for Bronwyn turned her head away as if to give her time to compose herself.

'Oh, I'm just your average twenty-year-old,' she managed after a moment. 'I think I'll go up now, Bronwyn. I am tired.'

'See you in the morning.'

The morning was fine, the soft mild air a promise for the summer, bees humming through the spicy thyme flowers edging the path outside the kitchen window. The air had a soft clarity which provided a perfect vehicle for the scents and muted sounds which floated on it. In spite of herself Linnet found her heart lifting. Love was hard, but even with a broken heart one could appreciate beauty. And there was her writing, the only time when she forgot her pain. Deep within her, in a secret recess of her being, she even allowed herself a tiny ray of hope. According to Bronwyn Justin had never had any intention of marrying her, so those rapturous moments he had shared with Linnet were cleaned of the taint which had clung to them.

Just honest lust, she thought, smiling a trifle bitterly at the clumsy movements of a bumble-bee.

Then the doorbell went, and she opened the door expecting to find Sarah there. Her heart beat a sudden, deafening tattoo in her throat, then slowed, for he looked as aloof as that first day they had met—aloof and unattainable, hard as granite.

'May I come in?' he asked after a moment.

'I—yes, yes, of course.' Hurriedly she walked in before him into the kitchen where the coffee pot was steaming fragrantly. 'Would you like a cup of coffee?'

'Yes, please.' He sat down at the small table in the window, watching her suddenly clumsy movements as she poured.

'You don't have sugar, do you?' she enquired stupidly, bringing the mug across to the table. 'Just milk.'

'Yes.' Justin waited until she had sat down, then stirred the coffee, asking calmly, 'Did you sleep well last night?'

'Yes, very well, thank you.' Why couldn't she think of anything but inanities to mouth?

'Good.'' Without hurry he drank some of the coffee, set his mug down and said, 'Linnet, I want you to marry me.'

Incredulous joy shot through her. Just for a moment she felt a rapture of certainty, until she met his glance and saw there nothing but calm enquiry.

It was as if his lack of emotion iced hers over too. In a low voice she said, 'No.'

'Why not?'

Could he not see that he was tearing the heart from her body? Or perhaps—humiliating thought—he realised her love, and thought his passion was enough to keep her happy!

'I don't have to answer that,' she replied with a small spark of spirit.

'I'd like to know why, nevertheless.'

God give me strength, she prayed with more fervour than she had ever experienced before. Aloud she said, wondering at the clear firmness of her voice, 'Because you don't love me and I—' swallowing before she could bring out the lie, '——I don't love you.'

'I see.' Oh, but he was calm! 'If I told you that I loved you would you believe me?'

'No,' she whispered miserably. 'We haven't had that kind of relationship at all. Whatever you've felt for me, Justin, it hasn't been love.'

He leaned across and pushed aside the strap of the suntop she wore, his eyes kindling with a cold fire as they found the marks where his fingers had gripped her the night before.

'Perhaps you're right,' he said slowly, pulling her with him as he rose from his chair, 'but it's very sweet, for all

that. Don't you feel you could take a chance on it turning
to love, Linnet?'

Mesmerised by the icy brilliance of his glance, the purpose she saw written there and shaping the sensual lines
of his mouth, she still had enough strength of will to say
loudly, 'No! And don't do this, Justin. . . . *please!*'

He smiled then. 'But I enjoy it. And so do you, my
darling, much as you hate me knowing it.'

In his eyes there were darker specks, islands of gold in
the pale grey which made them forbidding. They seemed
to blaze up now, engulfing Linnet in a devouring fire of
emotion from which she had no wish to escape. Very
dimly she could hear a thrush singing, the sound of a car
changing gear on the road—and then she heard nothing
more but the soft sounds of his breathing and a thunder of
heartbeats in her ears as his mouth sought each of the
marks inflicted by his fingers, as if to draw pain from each
one.

When the strap landed against her upper arm she
pulled back, but his arm across her back was strong and
he crushed her mouth beneath his, probing deep within
in a kiss that was as sensual as it was controlled. Dimly
Linnet realised that his lovemaking was coldly determined, that he was deliberately using all of the expertise at his command to reduce her to submission, but
she was caught by the twin snares of her love and the
response his sexuality induced from her body.

So her hands came up to cradle his head closer and
ever closer, and when his mouth left hers she whispered,
'Please—Justin——' not knowing what she asked for,
aware only that she did not care if he took her now, that
this ache which shook her body could only be assuaged
by complete union with him.

He smiled then, and ran his hands through her hair,
holding her head still while his mouth traced every sensitive pulse spot and hollow of her face, moving to her
throat and then to the gentle curves of her bared breasts.
Desire was a red tide of abandon, a weakening of every
muscle in delicious languor, a sensitivity of skin and

nerves which made her respond wantonly to Justin's hands and mouth with her own, kissing his shoulder as she pulled his shirt up so that she could rest against the hard warmth of his chest, her lips as soft and inviting as any courtesan of old.

Then he held her, cheek against cheek, while her body screamed with frustration and she could feel the cold film of his sweat against her hands, her face and her breasts.

'You see, you do enjoy it,' he said thickly, the words slurred with the passion she had aroused. With a merciless finger he tipped her chin up so that he could look into her eyes. 'If I kissed you now and kept my mouth on yours, I could carry you into your bedroom and make love to you and you'd give me everything I wanted, gladly, wouldn't you?'

His glance compelled an answer. 'Yes,' she said sullenly.

'Then why refuse my proposal?'

Bitterness choked her. 'Is that all that marriage means to you? Sex? No wonder your first attempt was unhappy!' she said cruelly, careless of his reaction now that his scheme was clear to her.

A line of white appeared around his mouth. 'You know nothing about that.'

'No. But I do know that you're trying to force me into a situation that I can't escape from.'

'If I'd wanted to do that I'd have accepted what you so freely offered a moment ago,' he returned with icy anger.

Incredible that they should stand like this, skin against skin, his arm across her shoulders, her hands across his back, lovers who hated each other. Linnet pulled away, yanking up the shirred sun-top to hide her breasts, her expression as cold and set as his, only the full redness of her lips marking the passion which had so nearly fused them into one being.

And yet, in spite of that mask she had donned, she knew that he had only to touch her again and she would melt just as swiftly, fired by a desire she could no longer control.

'It's just as well you didn't,' she said on an indrawn breath. 'I'd have been hating myself by now.'

Justin smiled, and said with a meaning look at his watch, 'Hardly, Linnet.'

Her blush was a rolling tide of colour which made her even angrier with him. 'Look, just go, will you!' she snapped, turning half away. 'I have things to do this morning, even if you haven't'. For some reason she added, 'I'm going down to the library.'

'Ah, yes.' He took his time about tucking his shirt back into his trousers, apparently not noticing the fact that she had walked abruptly into the kitchen.

Now she stood staring down at her hands, curling her fingers sharply into her palms to prevent them feeling the smooth dampness of his skin under them.

It took her some moments to realise that he had gone. Light-footed as a panther, he must have just walked out without bothering to close the door. Linnet shivered, wrapping her arms about her waist as though to keep warm while her brain raced futilely back and forth, mouse-timid, refusing to face the implications of the incredible scene which had just been enacted.

After a while she went across to the table, picked up the coffee cups, astounded to find his unfinished one still warm. It seemed an æon ago that he had sat there drinking it; so much had happened since.

Anger gripped her. How *dared* he come here and propose so coldly, as though a wife was something to be bought like a refrigerator. Like any good consumer, he had tested her first, she thought, lashing herself with her humiliation as she swirled detergent into the sink and deposited the dishes in the frothy water. Tested her—no doubt awarding so many marks for passion, so many marks for appearance, so many marks for anything else his cynical arrogance deemed important in a wife. As he must have done for Bronwyn too. Regardless of what her sister said, his reaction to the situation they had walked in on last night had been too violent for him to have been entirely indifferent, the marks on her shoulder were proof enough of that!

Impelled by the need to escape from the confines of the flat she hurried through the dishes, changed her clothes and pulled the door to behind her with no fixed notion of where she was going. There must have been some rain during the night, but the sky was cloudless now, the warm vibrant blue of early summer before the heat of summer fired it into a metallic bowl. A light breeze tugged at the pale tendrils against her cheek, cooling and refreshing. It was hot enough for a faint mist to rise from the tarseal of the drive, early enough for the birds still to be singing. There was even one vagrant tui, chirruping from the ferny branches of a jacaranda tree.

Very beautiful—it was unfortunate that as she passed the garage of Justin's house he should come out with Sarah clinging to his hand.

There was no dignified way of coping, especially not when Sarah squealed with joy and her father viewed Linnet with an ironic mockery which infuriated as well as shamed her.

She tried, however, responding to Sarah's greeting with a smile, ignoring the lifted eyebrow with which Justin signifed that he noticed her change of clothes.

'Where are you going?' Sarah asked eagerly.

Lashes lowered, Linnet replied, 'To do some shopping and then to the library.'

'Oh.' Sarah knew better now than to demand to accompany her, but her voice was wistful when she asked, 'Will you be back after lunch?'

'Yes.'

'Good.' She brightened instantly. 'I've got a bit stuck with that little duck around the beak.' Turning to her father, she told him confidentially, 'I've got a present for Anna's birthday hidden in Linnet's wardrobe. Linnet showed me how to make it. Daddy, I don't know what I'd do without Linnet now.'

Very deliberately he said, 'Perhaps you won't have to. I've asked her to marry me, but she's a bit hesitant.

You'd better see if you can persuade her to say yes.'

Above Sarah's ecstatic little body Linnet met the cold amusement of his gaze with seething accusation, but it was her eyes which fell first.

All that she said through stiff lips was, 'That's totally unfair, Justin.'

'Isn't there an old adage: "All's fair in love and war"?' '*Why?*'

But he said nothing, just kissed his daughter goodbye and left them.

When he came home that night Sarah was in bed, her temperature soaring while Anna wondered worriedly whether to call the doctor. Linnet was beside the bed sponging the woebegone little face with cool water, her expression shuttered to hide the anguish and anger she felt, her voice softly soothing the child.

Justin came straight in, kissed and cuddled his daughter with some resultant calming of her overwrought condition, then got to his feet.

When Linnet followed him from the room, 'Do you want to see me?' he asked politely, looking down from his greater height with a return to his former aloofness.

'Yes.'

'Then I suggest that the study will be the best place.'

Once there her eyes flew to the painting she had admired. Now she found its starkness unpleasant, the ruthless realism a mirror of the man who stood below it.

Without preamble she said, 'I'll marry you, but I'll never forgive you for the rotten methods you used to get your own way.'

He smiled at that. 'Very dramatic, but I'll bet that in twenty years' time you'll be wondering why you made all this fuss.'

'Justin, I mean what I say. I'll marry you, under duress. I shudder at the thought of spending the rest of my life married to a man who sees me as an ideal substitute mother for his daughter and only wants the most basic things from me, but I've no option now you've told Sarah.' The words tumbled over each other in the intensity of feeling; she was unaware that her hands were twisting together with the desperation of a distraught woman. After a moment of silence she ended numbly, 'I think I hate you.'

'I can cope with that,' he said with insolent honesty, 'as long as you respond as you did this morning.'

'*Must* you look at everything from that angle?' She knew that the contempt in her voice was angering him, but she was too angry herself to care any longer. Sarah's distress had been shattering enough to render the day a hideous turmoil of emotions and she felt that she must strike out at the cause of it all or explode with pent-up frustration.

'You've just told me that I see you as a sex object,' he returned indifferently. 'Is it feminine lack of logic which makes you flare up when I follow suit, or is it pique?'

'Go to hell!' she choked, furious that he had put his finger on the reason for her anger with such brutal accuracy.

'Gladly.' He laughed, came towards her and caught her in his arms, looking down at her with a kind of hard possessiveness. 'But you'll come with me, my beautiful firebrand.'

The kiss was brief, but quite long enough to convince Linnet of her inability to resist him. When it was over he smiled, 'So that's that. You'll——'

Sarah's voice was high-pitched, so accusing that both of them whipped guiltily around to face her as she stood, nightdress-clad, in the doorway.

'Why are you kissing each other?'

Her father moved across the carpet with his usual noise-less tread. 'Because she's just decided that she will marry me after all,' he told her gently. 'What are you doing out of bed?'

'I wanted to know what you were talking about.' Clinging on to Justin's hand, she stared unblinkingly at Linnet. 'Are you going to marry him?'

'Yes.'

An exhausted sigh shook the child's slender frame.

'Good. I'll go back to bed now. Daddy, you come with me. I want to tell you something.'

Bookshelves took up one of the walls; on the theory that you know a man best by his books, and to still the racing of her heart and brain, Linnet surveyed the volumes. Not many novels, although there were some obviously well-read classics, mostly from the eighteenth century. Typical, she thought. A century known for its hard logic and lack of romantic fervour. A large number of books about New Zealand ranging from an exquisite collection of hand-painted plates of birds to a very erudite tome on politics, all of the famous essayists and a range of books covering anthropology and archaeology, sociology and a few other -ologies as well. Not exactly a light selection, she decided. Rather astonishing to see an assortment of modern poets. Justin had plenty of other interests beside his business.

It struck her as strange that she knew very little about this business of his, apart from what Bronwyn had told her. Doyle Holdings could mean anything.

When he returned she was looking at a small paper-weight in the shape of a sinuously curved dolphin, her slender fingers touching the flowing silver with sensitive appreciation.

'Is she all right?' she asked, setting it back on the shelf.

'Yes. She's already asleep.' He moved a few papers around on his desk, then said briskly, 'I'll call for you at ten tomorrow morning and we'll select a ring. Did you go to the library this morning?'

Avoiding his eyes, she answered, 'No.'

'So you knew that this decision was inevitable.'

His voice was bland, but before she could reply he went on, 'You'd better go down tomorrow and tell the librarian you can't take the position. It's only fair to tell her before you let the City Council know. Now, do you know your mother's telephone number?'

'My mother's——? Yes, I do. Why?'

'I imagine she'll want to know before anyone else,' he observed mockingly. 'We'll put the call through now.'

As he dialled he kept his eyes on her, daring her to protest at this assumption of power. After the first involuntary gape, Linnet said nothing. She had given him the right to take over her life, so it was useless to feel outraged by this show of calm efficiency.

It took only seconds before he handed the receiver over to her, saying in a low voice, 'Try to sound a little more cheerful than you look, Linnet.'

Fortunately it was her mother who answered, her light voice forcing Linnet to realise just how much she missed her.

'Is everything all right?' she demanded sharply after the first exclamations of joy. 'Darling, are you well?'

'Yes, Mum, fine. Couldn't be better. As a matter of fact,' trying to ignore Justin as he wrote something on a memo-pad, 'I've just got engaged.'

'*Engaged*! But Linnet—love, you've only been over there a few weeks!'

'He's a fast worker,' Linnet told her, infusing her voice with what she hoped was the right amount of joy and wonder. 'His name is Justin Doyle.'

'What's he like?'

Wilfully ignoring the real meaning of her mother's question, Linnet let her glance rove over the man before her. 'He's about six feet two, with fair hair and very pale grey eyes, he's *very* handsome—' with a wry emphasis he could not miss—'and he is very rich.'

'*Linnet!*'

She laughed then, as much at the faintest suggestion of colour in Justin's skin at this catalogue of his physical attributes as at the shock in her mother's voice. 'Mum, he's standing here listening, so you can't expect me to go into a rapturous description of his virtues. It's bad for discipline. But he has an enchanting seven-year-old daughter called Sarah, so you'll have an instant step-grandchild.'

'Linnet, I'm coming straight across—tomorrow if possible. Now, please put him on. I want to speak to him.'

Linnet handed the receiver over, submitting with

something perilously like pleasure as Justin pulled her towards him. She allowed herself to relax, her head resting against the width of his shoulder.

'Mrs Perry? he said quietly. 'I'm Justin Doyle.'

The little voice at the other end chattered for a few seconds; Justin smiled. 'I'm quite harmless, I promise you. And I certainly know what I'm doing. I'm thirty-one. I know we've only known each other a short time, but I'm convinced that Linnet is what I need to make me happy.'

He sounded it, too; top marks for acting, Linnet thought sourly, suddenly exhausted and sickened by the blatant deception. She made to move away, was held in place by a merciless arm across her waist.

'Oh yes,' he was saying now, all smooth positiveness, 'she'll be happy with me. Yes, I'd be pleased if you could come, but you must allow me to fly you over—both of you, of course. I can put you up, as well. Bronwyn's flat is too small. My office in Sydney will contact you when arrangements are ready. Yes, I'll put her on. Goodbye, Mrs Perry.'

Linnet took the receiver again. 'Hello?'

'Well, he *sounds* very nice, Linnet. Are you sure, my dear?'

'Yes, I'm quite sure.' The lie stuck in her throat but she swallowed it manfully. 'Will you both come over?'

'Yes, of course. Goodbye, my darling.'

After she had replaced the receiver Linnet stood for a long moment while her throat ached with a need to be comforted, to be loved as she loved him.

'Tears?' he mocked, turning her to face him. 'Are you still harbouring the remnants of an adolescent passion for your stepfather?'

'Bronwyn told you,' she said without surprise.

'Yes, Bronwyn told me. What is he like, this husband of your mother's?'

'Very nice,' she retorted, angered by the cruel note of cynicism in his voice. 'Gentle, kind, compassionate . . .'

To her horror tears did gather behind her eyelids.

Sniffing inelegantly, she wiped them away with the back of her hand, not daring to look at him in case she broke down and bawled like a baby.

'Everything I'm not,' he taunted softly. 'Tough luck, Linnet. You've made your bed; now you'll have to lie in it. And if you know what's good for you there'll be no repinings.'

'I'm not afraid of your threats,' she retorted, wincing as his hands dug into the softness of her waist. 'I didn't make my bed, I was blackmailed into it. You might own me, but you'll never own my brain. I can think what I like.'

'Oh, certainly,' he laughed deep in his throat and kissed her, taking his time about it as he explored her mouth with the deliberate sensuality she so feared and hated.

At first she was rigid, refusing to respond, but her needs played the traitor and with a soft moan she brought her hands up to clasp his shoulders, swaying against him so that she was aware of his potent masculinity and then she was free, cold and trembling in the humid air.

'I don't imagine that you'll be thinking of anyone other than me when we make love,' he told her bluntly, seeming to enjoy her humiliation. 'Fight it as much as you can, Linnet, you're ready and ripe for love.'

'I despise you!'

'You don't despise me, you despise yourself, and that's your problem, not mine.'

'I might be frigid,' she cried, trembling with suppressed desire.

Justin smiled. 'I doubt it. You're a passionate creature in spite of your lack of experience. That's impossible to fake.'

'I might not be so lacking in experience.' She whirled around to face him, trying to look worldly and experienced. 'You don't know that I'm a virgin.'

'What's that got to do with anything?' His laughter was sardonic. 'I'm not a virgin, Linnet, and that doesn't worry you, does it?'

'It would worry you if your wife had slept with other men,' she retorted shrewdly.

His expression hardened into a mask, ruthless, almost savage. 'My wife, yes. But you'll be faithful to me—I'll see to that. As for what's happened before—' his massive shoulders lifted—'that's nothing to do with me. I'm no hypocrite; I haven't been exactly chaste. At the same time—' he observed calmly, 'I'm no fool either, and I know damned well that any experience you've had has been confined to a few kisses.'

'You *don't* know!' she flared. Anger and desperation, the closing of all avenues of escape, made her reckless so that she scarcely knew what she was saying.

He looked her over, as she stood, slender and straight before him, her emotions turning her eyes into pools of molten gold, the lips he had kissed flushed against the pale gold of her skin, red hair gleaming. In spite of his immense self-control his chest heaved with the sudden acceleration of his breathing, but whatever she had aroused in him was crushed, stillborn.

'Stop behaving like an idiot,' he said caustically, turning away to pick up the memo pad again. 'Sarah's tantrums are enough for one family.'

'Oh—oh!' Furious at this contemptuous dismissal, she found that she had to clench her fists tightly to stop herself from flying at him and belabouring him with all the strength of her frustration. 'I *loathe* you!'

'And I'm just about sick of you,' he retorted. 'What the hell do you want me to do? Prove to you that you're a virgin? Are you trying to make me jealous? If that's it, give it up, Linnet, before you find out that the game's not worth the candle.'

Something in his voice brought her back to cold sanity. 'As Alison found out?' she asked after a long tense moment.

His silence became dangerous. With his back to her he seemed threatening, yet there was nothing but cool agreement in his voice when he answered, 'As Alison found out. Why does Alison worry you so much, Linnet? You can't be jealous of her, that would mean that you love me, and you've told me you don't. Have you heard that scurrilous bit of dirt about her committing suicide?'

'I've heard it,' she answered honestly, 'but I don't believe it.'

'Why not?'

'Anna happened to mention that she loved Sarah. She wouldn't have tried to kill herself with her in the car.'

'You're right, of course,' he said, turning to face her. 'Alison loved life too much to take her own. Incidentally, I hope I don't need to tell you that Sarah has no idea of this—and God help anyone who tells her!'

'Do you think I'm likely to?' she asked scornfully. There had been no expression in his voice, but she felt suddenly cold.

'I'm just warning you. Now,' with an abrupt change of tone, 'have you had any dinner?'

'No. Sarah wanted me with her, and I wasn't hungry.'

'Then I suggest you share mine. Anna will be delighted to set another place for you.'

'I don't think——'

'Oh, for heaven's sake!' he snapped, his monumental patience cracking. 'Stop objecting to everything I suggest, will you? Let's try to behave like civilised human beings for once.'

Linnet bit her lip as she flung her head up defiantly, but allowed herself to be propelled out of the room, determined not to let him see just how much his anger affected her.

'There's a powder room in there,' he said, stopping beside a door in the hall. 'Go and do whatever it is you need to do to your face while I see Anna.'

The powder room was small and exquisitely decorated in gold and blue, an ornate little affair compared to the rest of the house, as if the decorator and the architect had combined to produce one frivolous room in contrast to the splendid austerity of Justin's taste. The light was excellent; too good, Linnet decided, peering at the tragic countenance the mirror revealed. No wonder he had suggested she do something to her face! Delicate bones were all very well, but they tended to sharpen one's features when under stress. She looked wan and miserable. Nobody seeing her now would accept that she had just become engaged to the man she loved with all her heart.

To her horror tears suddenly brightened the depths of her eyes, replacing with a film of iridescence the gold which seemed to have been smudged away.

'You are *not* going to cry,' she hissed at her reflection, then blew her nose, washed her face and combed her hair, wishing fervently that she had the sort of hairstyle one could hide behind. Or that she had brought some make-up with her to construct some sort of mask. Without anything at all to hide the too-open cast of her countenance she was far too vulnerable.

Justin met her at the entrance to the living room, an enormous, beautiful room, the essence of sophistication with its suede furniture in shades of cream and bone, travertine side tables and fireplace of cream stone. Above it was a painting, a Dutch landscape of the eighteenth century, the sparse, brilliantly executed foliage strangely at home in the very modern room.

'Who did your decorating?' Linnet asked after Justin had poured her a sherry.

One brow lifted. 'A friend of mine, Jan Duncan. I told her what I wanted, she drafted out a scheme and I approved—or not. Why?'

The sherry was very dry, superbly so. Linnet lifted brooding eyes from contemplation of the amber liquid and cast them around the room. 'It's the ideal background for you, she must know you very well.'

'She's an astute woman.' He dismissed the subject as if it bored him. 'If you dislike anything, you can change it.'

Linnet stared, then shrugged, 'I wouldn't dare. Anyway,' as she saw his brows draw together, 'I like the room. Especially that Chinese screen. Is it very old?'

She was gabbling, trying to prevent any more intimate conversation. Perhaps he sensed her exhaustion, for he replied in kind and kept his distance.

'Several hundred years. I have its history, if you're interested. Most people find it too sparse.'

'Oh no,' she said impulsively, picking up an exquisite piece of moon-green pottery. 'It's beautiful—no excess at all, and yet although it's so stark it's still human, isn't it.'

Oddly enough he seemed to understand her somewhat garbled words. 'The Chinese saw everything in terms of harmony,' he said, 'including man's relation with nature. That's why their landscapes are always humane. Also why they're so popular, I believe. Now finish your drink, or bring it in to dinner with you.'

CHAPTER NINE

WHEN she woke the next morning Linnet lay for a long time in bed, as if by not getting up she could hold the day at bay. But Justin wanted her ready by ten, so at last, reluctantly, she climbed out and showered, her mind recalling the meal last night.

Anna had already eaten; apparently she preferred to eat all her meals by herself, which meant that Justin must also eat by himself. His meals were not exactly social occasions, Linnet thought wryly, even when they were as well cooked as that of the night before.

As if she had known something Anna had set a small table out on the terrace overlooking a side garden redolent with the perfume of wallflowers and stocks. The table was a sensible size, not the usual rickety patio affair, and it had been decorated with a bowl of early roses, scentless, but exquisite in shades of pink and orange.

Justin had been a perfect host; there had been wine to go with the superb food, and after the coffee Linnet had slipped down to check on a now peacefully sleeping and quite cool Sarah while he had put a record on—one of her favourites, d'Indy's 'Symphony on a French Mountain Air'. It was unusual enough for her to be surprised at his possession of it, but at least it appeared that they had the same taste in music.

He had sat down beside her on the sofa, but had made no attempt to touch her, or move closer, except at the door of the flat, where he had bent and kissed her with all the passion of an uncle saluting his favourite niece.

Of course she was glad, she told herself, turning so that the stinging needles of water played across her face. She did not want him to kiss her as if he really loved her; that would be hypocritical. Although his passion excited her it also degraded her. Better by far to be treated with consideration, with respect. If her instinct told her that it couldn't last she ignored it, refusing to look any further than the ordeal of buying the engagement ring.

Naturally she chose her clothes carefully, finally settling upon a cream dress with a gently draped vee-neckline and long sleeves. It was more sophisticated than her usual clothes and the colour did wonders for her skin and hair, but even so she had to add blusher to hide the traces of a sleepless night.

The occasion wasn't as bad as she had expected, although it was harrowing enough. Justin was known there; that was obvious, as was the fact that although the manager was too well trained to reveal his curiosity he was definitely agog beneath the pleasantly deferential manner. And Justin must have been on the telephone, for they were met and whisked into a viewing room with all despatch while two trays of rings were brought in—none of them priced.

All of them obviously expensive. The glitter and sparkle frightened Linnet; she bit her lip as her eyes roved over the beautiful things, lowering her head so that neither man could catch her expression. But with that odd sensitivity she had noticed before, Justin sensed her unease.

'We'll choose,' he said, with a note of authority underlying the pleasant tones.

When the manager had gone he asked calmly, 'Do you see any that you like?'

Linnet bit her lip. 'They're all beautiful.'

She wouldn't have been surprised to hear impatience in his voice, but he seemed to have himself well in hand. 'Take your time.'

So she took her time. How well he understood her! The rings were none of them conventional; instead they were exquisite examples of the jeweller's art, none of them ostentatious, but all possessing that essential rightness which gladdens the eye.

Linnet sat quietly, touching nothing, her eyes roving across the rich brilliance with a wistful glance which only partly hid her sadness.

At last she realised that one particular ring held her eyes for longer and longer moments each time, a thing of topaz and diamonds with the sun in its heart.

As if her choice was made known to him by some esoteric method of communication—perhaps there was such a thing as E.S.P.—Justin stretched out his hand and picked up the glowing, glittering thing; it fitted perfectly. 'It's the same colour as your eyes,' he said matter-of-factly, and when Linnet looked up at him he kissed her briefly.

His mouth was warm and firm, the glance which rested on her flushed cheeks faintly ironic.

'It has a wedding ring to match,' he said. 'Do you want to see it?'

It fitted beautifully too. Without protesting Linnet tried it on, gave it up to the salesman, and agreed with Justin that a wide platinum band looked best on his finger. Somehow she had not thought that he would want to wear a wedding ring. Unbidden a query about his choice of a wedding band for his first marriage popped into her brain, bringing with it the shattering assault of jealousy which always accompanied her vision of Alison's lovely, laughing countenance. He had been madly in love with Alison, even if it had later turned to hatred; a far cry from the emotions he felt for his second wife.

Then they were out of the shop, and he was escorting her towards the car, observing that he had decided not to publish an announcement of their engagement until after her mother had arrived.

'And if she objects, I suppose you'll call the whole thing off?'

His smile was saturnine. 'You know me better than that, Linnet. I'll simply change her mind.'

'You must be the most conceited man I know,' she retorted sharply.

Justin laughed outright at that, real amusement colouring his voice. 'And you, my darling, rise so very swiftly to the bait. Don't you think I could persuade your mother that I'm suitable to be her son-in-law?'

Of course he could; Jennifer would be no match for him. But Linnet said stubbornly, 'She wants my happiness very much, and if she thinks I'm not happy she won't be at all agreeable.'

'I'm quite sure I can convince her that any hesitation she observes in you is mere maidenly modesty,' he observed with biting sarcasm.

'Oh, come off it! She's not——'

'Not particularly observant, certainly, or she would have noticed that her daughter had fallen in love with her fiancé.' He ushered her into a building, nodded at someone and stepped with her into a lift, pressing a button as the doors closed before turning to face her, his expression coldly speculative. 'From all that I've heard she sounds like a pleasant, scatterbrained creature with an enviable knack of viewing the world through glasses fashioned by her own needs and desires.'

He watched as Linnet struggled for words, the expressions chasing each other across the smooth contours of her face.

After a moment she turned away, facing for the first time the unpalatable fact that he had described Jennifer exactly.

But her love and loyalty made her say quietly, 'She loves me—and I love her.'

'I don't think anyone had questioned that,' he agreed, more gently. 'Even Bronwyn, who's hated her for years, credits her with maternal affection.'

'If you've got your information from Bronwyn you must remember that she fought a battle with my mother for the custody of my father,' Linnet said stiffly, angry that he should discuss her family with Bronwyn, aware that her anger was irrational, for after all, he had every right to discuss things with the woman he had thought of marrying.

'I know,' Justin smiled at her as the lift came to a halt. 'But she's an astute woman, your half-sister, able to see both sides to a question. And she was always fond of you. Now, I've a little work to do. Do you mind waiting for me?'

'A very conventional question,' she observed drily. 'You've hardly given me an option, have you? I'll wait if you'll tell me a little about what you do.'

'It's a bargain.'

His personal assistant was an attractive fortyish woman, a Mrs Cottle, who gave Linnet coffee, found a magazine and then left her in her office while she disappeared into Justin's sanctum. It was quite impossible to discover from her attitude whether Justin made a habit of bringing his girl-friends up here, so after a few moments Linnet gave up brooding and lost herself in the magazine, an interesting if somewhat heavy volume about exports.

She was still deep in one of the more fascinating byways, the growing of goats for mohair, when Justin appeared. A swift glance at her watch revealed that he had been gone an hour, but she had certainly not been bored. Exports were fascinating.

Determined not to give him any further openings to shoot his shafts at her mother, she chatted about the magazine as they dropped down in the lift. He seemed somewhat surprised by her interest; rather waspishly she decided that he was even more surprised by the fact that she could take an intelligent interest in such a subject.

However, the truce continued through lunch in a small, smartly casual restaurant noted for its magnificent salads. Justin told her about his business—an umbrella, so he said, for an assortment of interests ranging from farms to a plant which manufactured plastics from casein to a stud where racehorses were bred to win races in New Zealand, Australia, Europe and the United States.

It was a pleasant time, perhaps the least tense moments she had spent with him, but at last he said, 'We'd better be off. You have that librarian to see.'

And the trapped sensation was back, the feeling that her life was closing around her into a prison house, herself the prisoner of her own love and compassion.

'Cheer up,' he said, perceptive as ever. 'Tell her that you're engaged and she'll forgive you anything.'

Linnet stopped. 'You don't think much of women, do you, Justin?'

'By and large, no, but don't let your feminist instincts get the better of you. I don't think much of most men, either.'

She waited until they were in the car park beneath before retorting angrily, 'You must be the most arrogant man it's ever been my misfortune to meet! What the hell have you done, that you can afford to look down on the rest of humanity from your mountain?'

He lifted his brows, faint hauteur transforming him into someone very different from the pleasant lunch companion.

'I admire positive qualities,' he said crisply. 'And although I like individual people, I find it quite impossible to profess any affection for the human race as such, most of whom seem to be fools or hypocrites, or both. However, I'll admit that my comment about the librarian was unfair. I don't know her.'

Which left Linnet with a curiously cheated feeling. But she rallied, suggesting defiantly, 'What you mean is that people have to measure up to your standards before you'll accept them!'

'Unworthy of you,' he mocked. 'That applies to everyone. Even you, Linnet.'

Somewhat to her own astonishment she smiled. 'Yes, of course,' she conceded reluctantly.

And there the matter rested, although the curious exchange remained in the back of her mind throughout the rest of the day.

The interview with the librarian was unpleasant; Linnet felt that she had let her down and her guilt made her conscious of the ineptness of her excuse. She left the library shaken and depressed; it was as though the life she had chosen for herself had been forcibly snatched from her grasp.

Then she had to tell Bronwyn that she and Justin were engaged.

Bronwyn was very still after Linnet, losing any vestige

of tact she possessed, blurted out her bombshell. Then she turned towards her, her expression carefully schooled into placid acceptance.

'I'm not madly surprised,' she said, 'but, Linnet, are you sure you know what you're doing? Justin isn't your average Kiwi male, and any woman who takes him on is going to need a lot of luck. Remember what happened to his first wife.'

'I can hardly forget it,' said Linnet with a faint smile. 'But she didn't commit suicide, Bron.'

'Oh, I know *that*! Just the same, she had a very hard time of it, as anyone who knew them will tell you. Once she let Justin down, that was the finish; he had no more time for her. Apparently he retired behind that wall of ice he wears so effectively and no one could get through to him. She really did suffer, Lin. In her own way she was fond of him.'

'You make him out to be a monster,' Linnet returned in a low voice. 'Yet you were prepared to marry him.'

Her sister shrugged. 'I don't know that I'd have gone through with it, when it came to the crunch. But even if I had, I was one up on poor Alison. He loved her, Lin, was hopelessly, besottedly in love with her, so that when disillusionment came it was shattering. I knew he didn't love me, so there'd be no disillusionment.'

Linnet turned away from her sister's shrewd glance. There were beads of perspiration along her top lip, perhaps from the heat, perhaps because of the dangerous ground which Bronwyn had steered them on to.

Slowly she answered, 'That happened years ago, when Justin was very young. He's matured since then.'

'Of course,' Bronwyn said soberly. 'Goodness, I'm acting like the proverbial wet blanket, aren't I? Sorry, honey. I hope you'll both be very happy. Just promise me something, will you?'

'What?'

'Don't be so suspicious, it's not like you. Just that you'll keep up your writing.'

Linnet looked at her in astonishment. 'Well, yes, I

can't imagine life without it—but why, Bron?'

'Because I think you've got something. I've been reading it and really, I'm quite impressed. It's rather odd to discover that one's little sister can stir one to tears and make one laugh.' As if afraid that she had revealed too much of herself, Bronwyn bent and opened the door of the drinks cupboard, continuing airily, 'We'd better have something to toast your happiness in, hadn't we? Have you let your mother know yet?'

'Yes.' Linnet found it hard to speak of her mother now, still raw from Justin's unsparing summing-up of her character. 'She might be on her way here now.'

'I'll bet she is!'

For the next few minutes Bronwyn was cheerful, almost coy, obviously trying to make up for her less than flattering reception of the news of the engagement. Linnet reciprocated, her pride refusing to allow herself to reveal just how unsure she was. Then Justin came down, was urbane and very sophisticated with Bronwyn, before carrying Linnet off to dine with him and a riotously excited Sarah. Perhaps he understood how she felt, for when he took her back to the flat he held her for a moment outside the door in a grip as lacking in desire as that of a brother, and said quietly:

'You're as strung up as a puppet. Are you frightened of me?'

She shook her head, not knowing how to answer. 'Just—nervous.'

'Linnet, trust me.'

It was dark, but there was a moon behind the clouds. In its ghostly light she could see the dim outline of his features. Sorrow drenched her in a tidal wave of emotion; scarcely aware of what she felt she shivered. His arm tightened across her back.

'Well, Linnet?'

'I do trust you,' she blurted, shaken with a desolation she had no defence against. 'I just wish——' She stopped, for she had almost given herself away. '*I just wish you loved me,*' was what had trembled on her lips, but she knew that she could not lay her heart so bare to his scrutiny.

'What is it that you wish?'

'Nothing.'

But he was relentless. 'Tell me, Linnet.'

Hastily, improvising, she said warily, 'I just wish you hadn't forced this issue. It wasn't fair.'

He smiled rather crookedly. 'I told you that all's fair in love and war. You've called me ruthless often enough to know that I'm not used to waiting for what I want. I'm sorry if you feel cheated.'

Then movements inside brought them back to realities. Justin kissed her, briefly but with hard possession, and turned her to face the door.

But that night she lay awake for hours, wondering if he had really meant love, or whether he was merely using the quotation to calm her fears. Reluctantly she forced herself to admit that he had shown no signs of love, unless his uncaring habit of being able to read her thoughts and the rare moments of gentleness he showed her were indications of emotions deeper than desire. Which was certainly a fine piece of wishful thinking.

At least Sarah was happy, she thought drearily. And Justin must be, as he had what he wanted, a mother for his daughter and a wife who would be incapable of resisting her love for him.

So it was only Linnet who grieved. Perhaps two out of three wasn't bad as an average, but it was pretty miserable for the poor third. Or perhaps she would become hardened over the years and accept what Justin could give her with a degree of complaisance.

Strange that she should set so little store on his passion when he had the power to set her alive as she had never been before. For her peace of mind it would have been better had she never learned that without love passion was a mere excitement of the senses, but she could not regret the new maturity caused by her love. The question was, could she be content to give him all that he needed from her and not count the cost, to love and continue to love him when their marriage was based on such a shaky foundation? In all honesty she did not know.

One part of her brain told her to stop this useless torment, useless because the die was already cast; she was Justin's now as irrevocably as if she had been married to him. He was not a man to let his possessions go unless he tired of them, she thought wearily, recalling Alison and her unhappiness.

Alison! If only she could discover what had really happened to that weary ghost, buried but still walking. It was impossible, of course. Only Justin knew the facts, and try as she did, Linnet could not imagine him telling her anything about the disaster that was his first marriage.

Restlessly she turned between clammy sheets, finally got up and went out into the kitchen to get a glass of water. Up in the house a light burned; as she drank she endeavoured to work out which room had the wakeful occupant. Eventually she narrowed it down to the study.

A strange tremor ran through her as she wondered what Justin was doing there. Regretting things, perhaps. It was half-past one in the morning, always the time to summon up ghosts and fears, the black dog on your shoulder, empty husks of dead dreams, dreary projections of present into future—all of the horrors hidden behind the cupboard doors of the mind during the day.

Oddly enought she slept easily after that.

The cloud cleared overnight; summer came in with a peal of laughter, not the searing heat and dry aridity of high summer but with a soft lush radiance which cast a cloud of glamour over the city. After lunch it would be very hot. Outdoor workers would get their first hard sunburn of the year and the beaches at Kohimarama and St Heliers would be packed with swimmers.

Dressed appropriately in shorts and a sun-top, Linnet sat down to write, welcoming the discipline which prevented her from turning other things profitlessly over and over in her mind.

Two hours later she surfaced amidst the insistent ringing of the telephone, stared at it with dazed eyes for a moment, then wandered across to answer it.

It took her some moments to identify the little voice at the other end. When she did her astonishment made her break into whatever he was saying.

'Rob? Rob, what on earth is going on?'

'Thank God I've got somebody! The big house didn't answer, so they must be all out. Listen, Eiluned, can you go up to National Women's Hospital? Cherry's been flown in—something about the baby. She hasn't got anyone with her and I'd like someone to be there until I can get down.'

'Of course I'll go up.' Linnet disguised her shock and concern with a briskness she was far from feeling.

'Good girl!' He sounded immensely relieved. 'Let Justin know, will you? I'll be down in as short a time as I can, probably a couple of hours or so.'

A taxi was soon on its way; Linnet changed into an outfit which she hoped made her look older and more responsible.

Sarah had run down to tell her that she and Anna were shopping in Remuera all morning. Linnet scribbled a note telling Anna where she was, shoved it into the letter box, then ran to the impatient toot of the taxi. She could ring Justin from National Women's.

At the hospital they were pleasant, helpful, and totally uncommunicative, although Linnet managed to persuade them to at least tell Cherry that she was there before settling down in a chair to wait. Every so often she tried to ring Justin's office, but either the hospital's callboxes were full or the line into the office engaged.

Even Anna was not answering, or more likely, enjoying a nice long gossip with Sarah over tea and cakes. Sarah was now released from dietary restrictions and last night had been looking forward to a cream doughnut with immense anticipation. Anna knew of an extremely good coffee bar where the doughnuts were something special, so she had informed Linnet and her father during dinner, and that was probably where they were.

Meantime the minutes passed slowly into hours until at last a Sister came and looked somewhat severely at

Linnet.

'You're no relation, are you?' she asked.

'No, but her husband asked me to come. I don't think they have any close relations here. Sister, is everything all right?'

'Oh yes, she's fine.'

'And the baby?'

'It's all right too.' She frowned. 'She lives at Kawau, doesn't she?'

Linnet nodded. 'Yes.'

'Well, it could have been worse. At least it's a lot closer than Great Barrier Island, and an aeroplane is easier to ride in than an ambulance. Come on, you can come and see her, but only for a moment. She's pretty tired.'

Heaving a sigh of relief, Linnet followed her. 'She would have broken her heart if she'd lost the baby. They've been wanting one for ages.'

'Well, she's come through this without harm. With any luck there'll be no further trouble.'

Cherry looked drowsy and pale, but cheerful, greeting Linnet with a passable imitation of her usual warm smile.

'Hi!' Stooping to kiss her cheek, Linnet found a suspicious moistness in her eyes. 'Rob should be here any minute,' she offered, sitting down beside the bed.

'Poor darling, he nearly had a fit when he discovered he couldn't come with me. Eiluned, have you got in touch with Justin yet?'

'Not yet,' Linnet admitted. 'The phones both here and at the office are pretty busy, but I'll let him know, don't worry. I imagine he'll be along to see you.'

'He'll dwarf the place.' Kind dark eyes searched Linnet's face. 'You look a bit washed out yourself. What's happened to drive away that lovely Kawau glow of good health?'

A flush of colour touched Linnet's cheeks. She and Justin had agreed that there would be no formal announcement of their engagement until Jennifer arrived, but she felt a heel hiding it from Cherry.

However, she had barely opened her lips when Cherry

asked, 'Is it to do with Justin?'

'Ah—yes.' Linnet was upset to think that Cherry should have realised her hopeless love for him.

'Well, I hope you accepted him,' Cherry said gravely. 'He could do with a little happiness. Lots would be even better.'

Linnet's lashes flew up at this surprising statement.

With a soft laugh the other girl touched her hand. 'I'm not blind, and I happen to know him well in spite of that cold manner of his. I knew he loved you the first time I saw you together.'

Words could not have expressed Linnet's fury when the Sister came back at that moment to order her out. There could be no gainsaying her command, but oh, how she wished she had been granted an extra five minutes!

Once outside everything seemed to happen at once. Tearing along the shiny corridor came Rob, his usual placidity gone as if beyond retrieval. Sister took him in charge while Linnet went to try once more to contact Justin, this time with luck. He wasn't there, but his personal assistant took the message and promised to get it to him as soon as she could.

Outside the booth Linnet stood for a few moments, wondering what to do. It seemed unkind to go back home, yet she did not want to intrude upon Cherry and Rob and she had no right to make helpful suggestions. She did decide, however, to wait and find out whether Rob had a place to stay the night. So she sat down on the chair which had already borne her company through many minutes and composed herself to sit through yet more.

A gnawing feeling within made her realise that it was well after lunch-time. Wistfully she thrust the thought of food to the back of her mind, occupying it instead with an intensive examination of Cherry's astounding statement.

Somehow, while crediting Cherry and Rob with perhaps a greater knowledge of Justin than anyone else, she could not believe it. Nobody knew him well enough to be able to read any sign of love in that impassive counte-nance. Cherry must have seen his interest, the physical attraction which had sparked between them from the beginning, mistaking it for love.

She had convinced herself of this when he and Rob arrived simultaneously from different directions. With a thumping heart she hurried towards him, took strength from the reassuring clasp of his hand, and felt that if only they could face the world like this, handfasted, she could bear anything. But he put her back into the chair and made his way with purpose into the ward. Linnet was not in the least surprised to hear he was able to see Cherry for a moment. Within ten minutes both he and Rob had returned, and he was asking how long she was to be kept.

'About a week.'

'I see.'

Rob was frowning, one hand tapping impatiently on the wall. 'I'll get back tomorrow——'

'Why?'

'Well, to look after the place!'

'Don't be an idiot!'

Rob grinned. 'O.K., I won't insist on going back if that's the way you feel. Naturally I'd prefer to stay.'

'You'd better put up at the house. It's comparatively handy, and Anna's looking forward to seeing you.'

For the first time Justin's eyes moved to Linnet's face, cool, assessing, yet not unkind. 'I'll take you home, I think.'

'Thanks for coming,' Rob said to her, his smile warm and understanding. 'It made a big difference to Cherry to know you were here. She asked me to tell you, specially.'

'I'm glad I was able to come,' Linnet assured him earnestly.

And that was that, except that Justin took her hand as they made their way out of the building. Trying not to notice the amused indulgence in the looks from most people they met, Linnet found herself cautiously happy. If only Justin loved her!

To her considerable astonishment he did not take her

back to the house. Instead the big car turned north-west making towards the high citadels of the bush-covered Waitakere Hills, those ancient remnants of the vulcanism which had made the isthmus where Auckland lay.

Linnet opened her mouth to ask a question, took one look at Justin's uncommunicative profile and firmly closed it again.

When the road began to climb it was through stands of native bush regenerated from the wholesale rapine of a century ago. Tucked in amongst the trees were homes, some old and gracious, some new and fashionable; here were modern houses raised on smooth poles stained green with preservative, others quaintly colonial with high, tiled roofs and dormer windows and all of them thoroughly at home in their leafy retreats. And all of them shared the magnificent view over Auckland, the suburbs at the foot of the hills, leafy rows of vines in the wine-growing district at Henderson, the mother-of-pearl waters of the upper harbour and, beyond the North Shore, the outlines of the islands of the gulf with their euphonious names, Waiheke, Ponui, Titititi, Matangi, and the prominent cone of Rangitoto.

Passing the small centre of Titirangi they continued on for some miles before Justin swung off the road on to a drive almost literally enmeshed in damp herbage, overgrown by enormous rhododendrons beneath a canopy of taller trees whose branches met above the track.

Linnet waited apprehensively for some of the foliage to strike the car, but Justin negotiated through it without a vagrant twig so much as touching the paintwork. After a few moments the road debouched into a paddock lying to the north, warm, surrounded by stands of bush tall enough to shelter, yet still permitting that glorious view to be seen. Dotted about it were puriri trees and beneath them lay sheep and cattle, grateful for the shade.

The drive ended in a bricked courtyard behind a small, old house, well cared for yet clearly empty.

As Justin switched the engine off Linnet turned to him, her query plain in her expression.

'I used to live here when I was a boy,' he said, the words heavy-sounding in the quiet air. 'Let's get out and have a look.'

It was very still, very quiet except for the soft bleat of one of this year's lambs. Bees buzzed enthusiastically in old-fashioned daisy bushes; a jacaranda canopied the courtyard with blue as bright as the sky above.

'It's lovely,' Linnet breathed, wishing fervently that he would hold her hand again instead of impersonally guiding her across the bricks with his fingers at her elbow.

'My parents lived here most of my childhood. I left to marry Alison, but I've always hung on to it. The last tenants moved out a few days ago.'

The fragile bubble of happiness enveloping Linnet evaporated at the sound of Alison's name. Why, oh, why did he have to mention her now?

At first she thought they were going inside, but instead Justin pulled a hamper from the boot of the car and escorted her down a path at the side of the house to a garden which was gay with old-fashioned flowers, stocks and pansies and wallflowers, roses, pinks and marigolds, all mixed together in a splendid pot-pourri of colour and perfume and form.

In one corner was a summerhouse half hidden by a mass of pink mountain clematis. Justin directed Linnet's footsteps across the grass to it, set the hamper down, then put her into one of the wrought iron chairs there.

'Anna realised that you weren't likely to have had much lunch, if any,' he said blandly, 'so she's packed something for you. I'll have coffee.'

So she poured coffee for both of them, and discovered that Anna had put in several slices of bacon and egg pie, a salad with cherry tomatoes, wholemeal rolls and white peaches to finish with.

Suddenly Linnet was inordinately, ravenously hungry. As Justin drank coffee, seated on the broad plank balustrade which overlooked the garden so that she got an excellent view of the uncompromising line of his profile, she devoured pie and salad with all of the hunger of a healthy young body deprived too long of food.

At last, when sated, she heaved a huge sigh, poured herself coffee and asked tentatively, 'Would you like a peach? I'll peel one for you, if you like.'

His smile was a lazy answer. 'Yes, I'd enjoy one.'

The fruit was sweet with pinkish juice which threatened to run down her chin. Linnet grabbed a tissue, mopped it up and sighed again.

'Such heavy sighs. Feeling depressed?'

There was a hint of mockery behind the smooth tones which had the automatic effect of stiffening her shoulders.

'Not at all,' she answered politely, putting the remnants of her feast back into the hamper. 'Just full. I'm afraid I made a pig of myself.'

'Not in the least. Such enthusiastic singlemindedness is a pleasure to watch. Don't you have to worry about your weight?'

Made uneasy by the way his eyes lingered down the length of her body, she replied, 'Not yet, anyway. I daresay it will come. Justin, why did you bring me here?'

He didn't seem angered by the bluntness of her question. 'Because I want to talk to you, and there seems no other place where we won't be interrupted. Sarah will probably be furious when we get back as it is. I'm afraid her conception of our marriage was a blissful state where she had you entirely to herself with me as a kind of father in the background.'

There seemed to be no answer to that. Linnet moistened her lips and sipped her coffee, wondering uneasily just what he had to discuss with her that needed such solitude as this.

'Nothing to say?' he mocked. 'Surely you didn't share her misconception, Linnet?'

'No, of course not. I know that——' hesitating, searching for words which would not come, she ended lamely, 'I know that you want a proper marriage. Not one in name only.'

'I hope so. Anything else would be asking for trouble, and believe me, I've had enough of that to put me off it for the rest of my life.'

The edge in his voice caught her attention at once; it was rare to hear such emotion in the generally level tones. Over the rim of her coffee mug Linnet assessed him anxiously, caught an unexpected hint of weariness and felt that aching compassion which weakened her sternest resolutions.

Jumping to her feet, she went over to him, laying an impulsive hand on his arm. 'Justin, I don't want you to feel you have to—to pander to me. I know I was angry at the tactics you used to get me to marry you—but I can understand why you did. You do love Sarah very much.'

He smiled at that, his eyes silver-grey and very piercing.

'I do, very much, but I didn't stoop to such underhand tactics just to ensure her happiness. Sit down, Linnet, I want to tell you about my first marriage.'

Chilled by what amounted to his rejection of her overture, Linnet seated herself on the chair, turning so that all that he saw of her was her profile. Two, she thought dully, could play at that game.

'I married Alison because I was infatuated with her,' he said, his voice cold and remote, totally without emotion. 'She was gay and beautiful, a restless, wayward, headstrong creature, vital and alive. I was too young to realise that what I thought was love was merely calf-love; I wanted her more than I'd ever wanted a woman and I determined to make her mine.'

Linnet found that her temples were cold with a dew of perspiration. She had wanted to know of that first marriage, but it was agony to hear him discuss the intensity of his feelings for Alison, knowing that this time he had decided to marry for infinitely more practical reasons.

'So we were married,' he said flatly. 'I suppose it took me a year to force myself to admit that I'd made the most colossal mistake, that my selfishness had cost her any hopes of happiness as well as my own. She was unstable, a victim of her own mercurial character and her parents' indulgence. By then she had become totally dependent on me for some sort of stability, and I——' he stopped, as if even now it went against the grain to admit his mistake, continuing after a moment in a flat voice, '——I had discovered that all that I could feel for her was a compassion which hurt me as much as it did her. She was pregnant, so there was no possibility of a separation. I'd like to be able to say that I accepted the situation gracefully and made the best of it, but that would be lying.'

Linnet sat with bowed head, wishing she could rid herself of the corroding envy which had her in its grip. Whatever had happened afterwards, Alison had known what it was like to be passionately adored by Justin; Linnet could not help feeling that she would give up almost anything to be the focus of such white-hot emotions. But he had made sure that nothing so heart-wrenching should every happen to him again.

For the life of her she could not speak, could not offer him any encouragement, certainly had no way of summoning up the words to silence him, which was what she wanted to do. With fingers tightly clasped around her coffee mug she stared into the amber liquid.

'I hurt her, again and again, because I couldn't hide my indifference,' he continued still in the same monotone. 'She reacted by behaving outrageously, so I treated her with a brutality which makes me cringe now when I think of it. The only excuse I have is that I was young, and not accustomed to disappointment.'

'You don't have to excuse yourself to me,' Linnet murmured in a choked voice.

'I want you to understand. I know you've heard— gossip. Your compassion and understanding led you to discount the most slanderous, but I feel that for her sake as well as mine you should know exactly what happened.' His voice altered, became dry with sarcasm. 'Of course, I can only put my side of things. You're at liberty to believe me or not.'

'I've never known you to lie,' she returned honestly.

'I can lie by omission as well as the next man,' was his unexpected reply. 'However, in this case I'm trying to be as objective as possible. When Sarah was born Alison was delighted; she became devoted to the child, and for a few months I hoped there was a chance of happiness for us all. Unfortunately she was unable to live up to her own high standards, and the moods of depression became more frequent, the periods of wild gaiety fewer and fewer. We moved to the country then; I'd hoped that the more settled life would help her. For a while it seemed to work; she flung herself heart and soul into life there, but when the novelty wore off she relapsed into her old ways and we had a constant stream of visitors invited by her to shield her from her own fears and inadequacies. If I'd loved her I might have been able to help, but I could only think of her as another Sarah, someone to protect and cherish.'

Linnet lifted her head, swivelling around so that she could see him clearly. The sun was westering now, casting longer shadows across the lawn, gilding his profile and throwing the rest of his face into darkness.

Very quietly, because her heart was racing so violently that she was sure he must hear it, she asked, 'Do you feel guilty about that, Justin?'

'I feel I failed her,' he answered, each word hard and clear on the soft air. Incongruously from somewhere in the paddock a skylark rose singing, the brilliant fountains of sound a hymn to the fertile warmth of the season as the bird followed an instinct as old as time.

Linnet asked carefully, 'Why? You seem to have done all you could to make her happy. Why do you think you failed her?'

Slowly he turned his head. His eyes held hers in a relentless glance. 'Because I insisted on marrying her,' he said.

Like the skylark, Linnet possessed instincts, and like him, she followed them. 'Then why the *hell* are you doing it a second time round?' she almost shouted, thumping her coffee mug down on the table.

Justin swung himself down on to the bricks of the floor, caught her shoulders and without slackening his grip drew her up into his arms. 'Because I love you,' he said, his expression stern and unyielding. 'And because I think you love me.'

'And if I don't?'

He laughed then, not with amusement but as if his tension was so great that only laughter could ease it. 'Then I'll have to teach you how,' he said. 'Because I know I can't live without you, and I'm damned sure that an emotion as strong as this must be reciprocated, even if you are too blind and obstinate to see it.'

'You're an idiot,' she said with loving emphasis, touching the firm line of his mouth with her forefinger, thrilled that his incredible avowal had given her the right to do this. 'Of course I love you, Justin. I——'

His mouth crushed her admission into nothingness; his arms strained her to him with a ferocity which made her gasp, but she hugged him as hard as she could, offering up her mouth and body to the searching punishment of his.

'I'm sorry,' he said deeply, after a while. 'Did I hurt you?'

'I don't care.' Linnet's eyes were slumbrous with quickly aroused passion, her voice deeper by several tones. She pressed a kiss on to the tip of his chin, whispering against the soft roughness of his skin. 'When did you know, Justin?'

'When I first saw you.' He smiled at her widened eyes. 'Surprised? Not as stunned as I was, believe me. You stood there on the doorstep, enough like Alison to rouse my antagonism, yet with that fundamental air of strength, and I knew that life was never going to be the same again.'

'You were so rude to me!'

He smiled, ironically, as one hand moved slowly from her throat to the curve of her breast, resting there with the stillness of complete possession. 'I was knocked off my feet. At first I thought it was merely physical, that perhaps I was doomed to want slim red-haired creatures with hazel eyes and the kind of sensuality which is as unconscious as it's provocative. And of course Bronwyn told me you were contesting your father's will.'

Incredible to think that she should ever see those silver eyes soften into tenderness! It was this which convinced Linnet that he really did love her; his passion, exciting and full of promise though it was, could not give her the happiness which that astounding gentleness brought into being.

Breathlessly, for his restless hand was roving as if trying to memorise the contours of her body, she said, 'I didn't contest the will, Justin.'

For a moment his lips tightened, then he nodded. 'I should have known, I suppose. No one could have looked at me with such fearless honesty and been underhanded. As it happens, I'm not sure you aren't entitled to your share, anyway.'

'I don't want anything,' she declared swiftly, while her heart sang with the knowledge that he had learned to love her in spite of Bronwyn's lie.

'No, it's not necessary.' He smiled, turning his head to the soft part of her wrist where a pulse throbbed invitingly.

'I knew that Bronwyn had summed me up as a prospective husband, of course, and to be quite honest I was half inclined to see things her way. Since Alison died I'd been careful not to let emotions ever enter into any relationships I'd formed; Bronwyn was ideal in almost every respect except that Sarah didn't like her.' His hand tightened painfully across her back for a moment, then relaxed to resume its slow sensuous stroking of her skin. 'I no longer believed in love, so a sensible marriage was in order, but I knew damned well that it would be far from sensible to marry her and hope for the best. Unfortunately, by the time Sarah's dislike became clear Bronwyn was a fixture. And your arrival on the scene queered things even more.'

'Why? Because Sarah liked me?'

'Partly.' With deliberation he held her away from him, his expression changing to encompass a hunger which frightened as much as it exhilarated her.

Never in her life had she dreamed that any man would search her face with such brooding intensity, that Justin of all people would tremble with a desire he could barely suppress! The strength of his emotions invoked a response which widened her eyes, brought a flush to her skin. Beneath her fingers she could feel the muted thudding of his heart, the tightly reined passion which he refused to unleash.

Her breath came sharply as she whispered his name, only to find herself forcibly turned away.

'Don't look at me like that,' he said harshly, thrusting his hands into his pockets as he leaned back against the balustrade. 'You're too beautiful—and I've waited for you too long.'

She had to smile at this. 'Darling, my mother is certain to say we haven't known each other for long enough!'

'All my life?' He smiled, the mockery back but this time without any intent to hurt. 'That's how long I've waited.'

'Oh—*Justin*!' Turning, she rested her head against his shoulder and hugged him fiercely to her, her voice muffled as she said, 'That's the most beautiful thing I've ever heard. Justin, I do love you, with all my heart.'

She could feel the fists his clenched hands made within his pockets as he answered, 'I wish I could come to you without the fiasco of my first marriage to mar things for you—or the fact that I was involved with Bronwyn.'

His shirt was of very fine cotton, smooth and pleasant against her skin. Linnet searched for the right words, then said honestly, 'I love Sarah, so I can't regret your first marriage, even though I was jealous of Alison. I didn't know anything about her except that you'd loved her, and I wanted so much for you to love me. And I knew you didn't love Bronwyn—she said as much herself. Darling, you say you love me—that's like a miracle. I don't care about anything else!'

She must have convinced him, for she could feel the tension ease away from his body. After a moment his hands found her shoulders, held her against him as he murmured endearments against her mouth as if she had given him a gift beyond price, as if he had never known what it was to love; he was almost hesitant, and the last ache of jealousy in Linnet's heart dissolved, washed away by the knowledge that for him this, too, was new and uncharted territory.

For a long time they stood quietly, passion checked, completely happy in their love, until at last he stirred.

'Dearest love, it's time we left. Your mother will be here at nine o'clock tonight, and we'd better be there in time to meet her.'

'Oh dear!'

Linnet looked so woeful that he laughed softly and kissed her with a restrained impatience which revealed just how much he held himself in check. 'There will be other times, darling.'

'I know.' She looked around with eyes which gilded everything they saw with the shining aura of her love. 'Justin, what made you decide to tell me—today—that you loved me? I didn't know. You were so—so *distant* with me!'

'If you knew how difficult it's been to keep my hands off you,' he answered grimly. 'Right from that first day— but especially after I'd delivered you to Kawau and kissed you. You fitted into my arms so satisfactorily, I knew I had to have you. But I didn't realise it was love and I blew it. Then when I found you in the kitchen there, and you responded so ardently, I acted like a clumsy kid in the throes of his first love affair and tried to seduce you.'

'Why?' she asked softly, remembering the pain and shame her open response to his lovemaking had caused her.

Shrugging, his deep tones even, he said, 'Because I wanted to punish you by reducing what had happened between us to its crudest ingredient, simple passion. I'd lost control, and refused to accept that my feelings for you were something far more earth-shaking than the greedy desire I'd thought was love.' He smiled thinly at the shock in her expression. 'Darling, I can be as illogical as any man caught in something bigger than he is. After I'd left you that night I sat on the edge of my bed and faced some pretty unpalatable facts. I'd known from the start that I wanted you, what I discovered then was that because of my own suspicion and my refusal to admit the difference between lust and love, I'd got things into an almighty tangle. But I knew I loved you, and I was almost certain that you loved me, that you'd got over that childish infatuation for your stepfather.'

Shaken by the depth of feeling in his usually impassive voice, Linnet laid her cheek against his hand. 'How did you know that?' she asked, trying to ignore the soft rhythm of his fingers against her skin.

'I loved you so much, I couldn't believe you were indifferent. And your response to me was swift and very sweet, as if you'd been waiting for me to touch you. So I decided you would have to marry me.'

'And you used despicable methods to force me to!'

'Yes.' He sounded sombre, but after a moment went on, his lips against her forehead, 'I'm sorry if I spoiled things for you. I didn't intend to use Sarah, but when you refused me I was desperate. After that I daren't risk a rebuff; if I'd told you I loved you and you'd said you felt nothing like that for me I'd have had to let you go. When Cherry said——'

'Cherry? What did Cherry say?'

'Merely that if I didn't tell you how I felt I had only myself to blame if you thought that I was marrying a mother for Sarah.'

'How did she know?' Linnet breathed. 'She told me you loved me.'

He shrugged. 'She's a very astute lady, thank God, and I'll be grateful always for her advice today. But even Anna knew. She was fully prepared to dislike you at first; she hadn't much time for Bronwyn. Then you won her heart with your laughter and your honesty and your kindness . . . Dear heart, I'll never be able to tell you how much I love you.' His hands cupped her face, turned it up towards his, his expression of such devouring intensity that she felt a weakness which was submerged instantly by her desire to make him as happy as he had made her.

'I do love you,' she responded swiftly, pressing a kiss on the corner of his mouth. 'What I felt for David was a—a kind of preparation for this, I suppose, affection and respect, but there was nothing—*nothing* like the response you forced from me.' Her colour rose, but she disregarded it, impelled by a need to convince him of her feelings. 'When you touch me I feel as though I'm drowning in a tide of sensation and I want more than anything to . . . to . . .' she stumbled, but went on bravely, 'I want you too, Justin. I didn't know it was possible to ache for anyone as I've ached for you.'

He laughed then, softly, victoriously, and lifted her in his arms as his mouth explored the sweetness and promise of hers. Almost lost in the matchless rapture of his love, she thought momentarily of Sarah, who would at last have the family she had yearned for. Then she gave herself entirely up to the exultant fierceness of Justin's hands and mouth; gone was the pain and the misunderstanding and the dislike which had had to be whipped up to hide a greater emotion. Ahead lay the future, fair and full of hope, but at the moment it was the present only which mattered. And that was paradise enough.

Harlequin Plus

A WORD ABOUT THE AUTHOR

Robyn Donald cannot remember ever being unable to read. She learned the skill at a very early age; and today, she claims, reading remains one of her great pleasures, "if not a vice."

Robyn, her husband and their two children make their home in a small country village in the historic Bay of Islands in the far north of New Zealand. Both the climate and the people are friendly, and her family enjoys sailing in particular and the outdoor life in general.

Her other interests include cooking, music and astronomy. And she finds history and archaeology especially fascinating because "they are about the sum total of human experience."

When she writes, Robyn visualizes scenes that she knows and loves. The actual germ of a story arrives "ready-made from some recess of my brain, but," she adds, "it takes quite a while to work out the details!"

Now's your chance to discover the earlier
books in this exciting series.

Choose from this list of great
SUPERROMANCES!

SUPERROMANCE

Complete and mail this coupon today!

- -

Harlequin Reader Service

In the U.S.A.
1440 South Priest Drive
Tempe, AZ 85281

In Canada
649 Ontario Street
Stratford, Ontario N5A 6W2

Please send me the following SUPERROMANCES. I am enclosing my check or money order for $2.50 for each copy ordered, plus 75¢ to cover postage and handling.

- ☐ #1 END OF INNOCENCE
- ☐ #2 LOVE'S EMERALD FLAME
- ☐ #3 THE MUSIC OF PASSION
- ☐ #4 LOVE BEYOND DESIRE
- ☐ #5 CLOUD OVER PARADISE
- ☐ #6 SWEET SEDUCTION
- ☐ #7 THE HEART REMEMBERS
- ☐ #8 BELOVED INTRUDER

Number of copies checked @ $2.50 each =	$_____
N.Y. and Ariz. residents add appropriate sales tax	$_____
Postage and handling	$_____ .75
TOTAL	$_____

I enclose_____.
(Please send check or money order. We cannot be responsible for cash sent through the mail.)
Prices subject to change without notice.

NAME_____
(Please Print)

ADDRESS_____

CITY_____

STATE/PROV._____

ZIP/POSTAL CODE_____

Offer expires May 31, 1982   109563323